CALIFORNIA
Diagnostic and Placement Tests

X #
% 2+a5=

 Glencoe

New York, New York   Columbus, Ohio   Chicago, Illinois   Woodland Hills, California

The McGraw-Hill Companies

 Macmillan/McGraw-Hill
Glencoe

Send all inquiries to:
Glencoe/McGraw-Hill
8787 Orion Place
Columbus, OH 43240-4027

ISBN: 978-0-07-878900-7
MHID: 0-07-878900-1   *California Diagnostic and Placement Tests*

Printed in the United States of America.

1 2 3 4 5 6 7 8 9 10   009   16 15 14 13 12 11 10 09 08 07

Table of Contents

This booklet is designed to be used in two ways.

- The eleven tests in this booklet provide tools to assist teachers in making placement decisions within Glencoe's Mathematics series for Kindergarten through Algebra 2:

  California Mathematics: Concepts, Skills, and Problem Solving, Grade K
  California Mathematics: Concepts, Skills, and Problem Solving, Grade 1
  California Mathematics: Concepts, Skills, and Problem Solving, Grade 2
  California Mathematics: Concepts, Skills, and Problem Solving, Grade 3
  California Mathematics: Concepts, Skills, and Problem Solving, Grade 4
  California Mathematics: Concepts, Skills, and Problem Solving, Grade 5
  California Mathematics: Concepts, Skills, and Problem Solving, Grade 6
  California Mathematics: Concepts, Skills, and Problem Solving, Grade 7
  California Math Triumphs: Intervention for Intensive Students, Grade 4–7
  California Algebra Readiness: Concepts, Skills, and Problem Solving
  California Algebra 1: Concepts, Skills, and Problem Solving
  California Geometry: Concepts, Skills, and Problem Solving
  California Algebra 2: Concepts, Skills, and Problem Solving

- These tests also provide valuable diagnostic information teachers may find helpful throughout the school year. See Learning Objectives before each test in this booklet for further information on using these tests as diagnostic tools.

- These tests are also available in Spanish at www.glencoe.com.

Placement Decisions

In making placement decisions for a student, consider a variety of evidence, such as the student's mathematics grades, classroom observations, teacher recommendations, portfolios of student work, standardized test scores, and placement test scores. Use the results of these placement tests in conjunction with other assessments to determine which mathematics course best fits a student's abilities and needs.

These tests can help determine whether or not students need intervention as well as the level of intervention required. Through strategic intervention, teachers can work with students using on-level content, but strategically choose which content strand(s) need further development. Sometimes, a student may struggle with a particular strand, but overall the student is able to perform on-level.

Intensive intervention is used with students who are struggling with most or all strands of math content and are unable to work on grade-level. These students will need alternative intervention materials to help meet their needs. These materials, such as the *Math Triumphs* programs, offer alternatives that will accelerate achievement in mathematics.

Test Content

These placement tests measure ability, but they are not achievement tests. They cover prerequisite concepts, not every concept found in a Glencoe mathematics textbook or in your state standards.

Mathematics concepts are introduced, developed, and reinforced in consecutive courses. These placement tests measure student mastery of concepts and skills that have been introduced or developed in the student's current mathematics course, that are further developed in the next course, but that are not developed in the following course.

For example, in the Algebra and Functions concept of *using variables* in Grades 5, 6, and 7, the concept is developed in Grade 5 and further developed in Grade 6, but it is only reinforced in Grade 7. If students have mastered simplifying fractions, Grade 7 content might be appropriate for them, but if they have not, Grade 6 content would better meet their needs.

In most situations, these placement tests are given near the end of the current course, in order to help determine student placement for the following year. Many teachers also use diagnostic tests in order to assess the needs of individual students as well as to assess overall math abilities of an entire class in the beginning of a school year. Additionally, these tests can be used in special situations, such as a student transferring into the school mid-year or entering middle school with advanced mathematics ability.

Placement Tests Format

Placement Tests for Kindergarten through Grade 2 use a similar format. All of the tests are oral tests and are divided into four parts:

- Number Sense
- Algebra and Functions
- Measurement and Geometry
- Statistics, Data Analysis, and Probability

The Kindergarten and Grade 1 tests each contain 15 questions. Teachers should read the directions, problems, and all answer choices (as appropriate) aloud, as students follow along. The Grade 2 test contains 30 questions. Students should read the directions, problems, and answer choices themselves, unless special circumstances warrant teacher assistance. The Kindergarten requires students to follow simple directions in order to answer each question, while the Grade 1 and Grade 2 tests are multiple-choice.

Placement Tests for Grades 3 through Algebra 1 use the same format. Each test contains 30 multiple-choice questions and is divided into four parts:

- Number Sense
- Algebra and Functions
- Measurement and Geometry
- Statistics, Data Analysis, and Probability

Placement Tests for Geometry and Algebra 2 use similar formats. Each test contains 30 multiple-choice questions. The test for Geometry is divided into four parts:

- Number Properties, Operations, Linear Equations
- Graphing and Systems of Linear Equations
- Quadratics and Polynomials
- Functions and Rational Expressions

The Algebra 2 test is broken down into eight parts to separate the Algebra 1 portion from the Geometry portion.

When interpreting scores on the placement tests, consider the student's score on each part, as well as the total score. Scoring Guide Masters before each test can be reproduced and used to record each student's score. A sample of a completed Scoring Guide for Grade 5 is shown below; a sample for Algebra 1 is provided on the next page.

The shaded boxes show the range of scores that corresponds to each placement option. If a student's scores on each part of the test fall in the same shaded range, then that course is probably the best placement decision. If a student's scores fall in different ranges or near range boundaries, then analyze the results for each part and use additional assessment results to help determine placement.

Sample Score and Placement Analysis

Sample Score: On the Grade 5 test, this student scored 10 questions correct in Number Sense, 6 in Algebra and Functions, 3 in Measurement and Geometry, and 2 in Statistics, Data Analysis, and Probability. The total number correct was 21 out of 30.

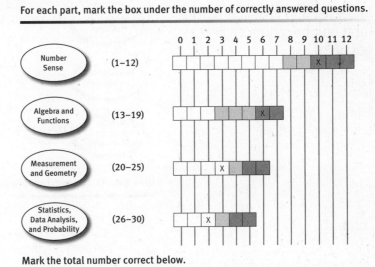

Mark the total number correct below.

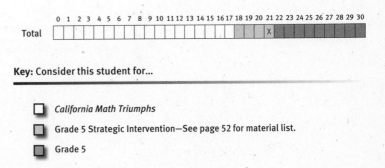

Key: Consider this student for...

☐ *California Math Triumphs*

▨ Grade 5 Strategic Intervention—See page 52 for material list.

▩ Grade 5

Sample Analysis

This student scored high on the first two parts but scored lower on the last two parts. If these results are similar to other assessments, this student is likely to need intervention materials for Grade 5 but will likely find Grade 5 too challenging without any intervention materials.

Scoring Placement Test for Algebra 1

Students who score in the Algebra 1 range for each of the four parts are ready for Algebra 1. Students who score in the Algebra Readiness range or below in each of the four parts, are best served by Algebra Readiness.

To place students who score in the Algebra 1 range on only two or three parts, use other factors, such as previous mathematics grades and teacher recommendations.

Sample Score and Placement Analysis

Sample Score: On the Algebra 1 test, this student scored 10 questions correct in Number Sense, 10 in Algebra and Functions, 1 in Measurement and Geometry, and 1 in Statistics, Data Analysis, and Probability. The total number correct was 22 out of 30.

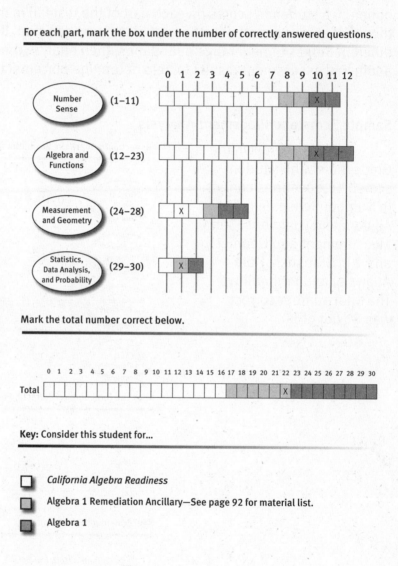

For each part, mark the box under the number of correctly answered questions.

Mark the total number correct below.

Key: Consider this student for...

- ☐ *California Algebra Readiness*
- ◻ Algebra 1 Remediation Ancillary—See page 92 for material list.
- ◼ Algebra 1

Sample Analysis

This student could be placed in either algebra course. This student will likely do well in *Algebra: Readiness*, but many find *Algebra 1* challenging. This student may need additional help to succeed in *Algebra 1* since the last two parts show relatively low scores. Check which questions were missed and consider other factors, such as English language or reading difficulties.

These placement tests also provide valuable diagnostic information for classroom teachers. Reproducible learning objective charts list the learning objective for each test question and can be found before each test. By marking each question the student answered incorrectly, you can see which objectives the student has not mastered.

Glencoe's wide variety of supplementary materials, such as the Skills Practice worksheets, Practice worksheets, and Problem Solving Practice worksheets available in the *Chapter Resource Masters*, and the ExamView® *Assessment Suite* CD-ROM, can provide intervention and remedial help. Diagnostic charts for each test, found with the learning objectives pages, describe the intervention that students may require and include a list of Glencoe print and technology materials.

If these tests are given near the end of the student's current course, it is recommended that the diagnostic information be shared with the teacher of that student's next course, in order to provide appropriate intervention during the next year.

Placement Test
Scoring Guide
K

Student Name _____

For each part, mark the box under the number of correctly answered questions.

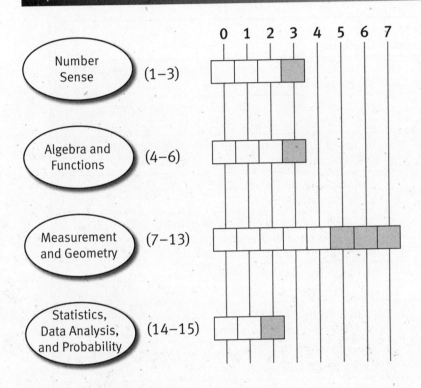

Mark the total number correct below.

	0	1	2	3	4	5	6	7	8	9	10	11	12	13	14	15
Total																

Key: Consider this student for...

☐ Strategic Intervention—See page 4 for materials list.

▨ Kindergarten

Placement Test K

Learning Objectives

Student Name _____

In the column on the left, mark the questions that the student answered *incorrectly*.

Strand	May Need Intervention	Objective
Number Sense	☐ 1	count with understanding and recognize how many in sets of objects
	☐ 2	count with understanding and recognize how many in sets of objects
	☐ 3	understand meanings of operations and how they relate to each other
Algebra and Functions	☐ 4	sort, classify, and order objects by size, number, and other properties
	☐ 5	recognize, describe, and extend patterns such as sequences of sounds and shapes or simple numeric patterns and translate form one representation to another
	☐ 6	analyze how both repeating and growing patterns are generated
Measurement and Geometry	☐ 7	recognize, name, build, draw, compare, and sort two- and three-dimensional shapes
	☐ 8	describe attributes and parts of two-and three-dimensional shapes
	☐ 9	describe, name, and interpret relative positions in space and apply ideas about relative position
	☐ 10	find and name locations with simple relationships such as near to and in
	☐ 11	recognize geometric shapes and structures in the enviroment and specify their location such as, above, below, next to
	☐ 12	recognize the attributes of length, volume, weight and area
	☐ 13	compare and order objects according to the attributes of length, volume, weight and area
Statistics, Data Analysis, and Probability	☐ 14	sort and classify objects according to their attributes and organize data about the objects
	☐ 15	sort and classify objects according to their attributes and organize data about the objects

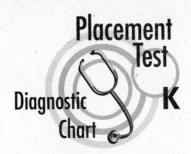

Student Performance Level	Number of Questions Correct	Suggestions for Intervention and Remediation
Strategic Intervention	0–9	Use additional Intervention and Remediation materials listed on the next page. This list of materials can provide helpful resources for students who struggle in the traditional mathematics program. Strategic intervention allows students to continue to remain in the *California Mathematics: Concepts, Skills, and Problem Solving* program, while receiving the differentiated instruction that they need. Teaching Tips and other resources may also be listed in the Teacher Wraparound Edition.
Kindergarten	10 or more	Use *California Mathematics: Concepts, Skills, and Problem Solving*. This student does not require overall intervention. However, based on the student's performance on the different sections, intervention may be required. For example, a student who missed 6 or more questions in the Measurement and Geometry section may require extra assistance as you cover these skills throughout the year.

A Special Note About Intervention

When using diagnostic tests, teachers should always question the reason behind the students' scores. Students can struggle with mathematics concepts for a variety of reasons. Personalized instruction is recommended for English language learners, students with specific learning disabilities, students with certain medical conditions, or for those who struggle with traditional instructional practice. Teachers should always consider the needs of the individual student when determining the best approach for instruction and program placement.

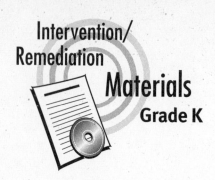

Intervention/Remediation Materials
Grade K

Print Materials

Reteach Masters	A brief explanation, along with examples and exercises, for every lesson in the Student Edition. These masters are included in the Chapter Resource Masters.
Skills Practice Masters	Additional practice in computational and application exercises for each lesson in the Student Edition. These masters are included in the Chapter Resource Masters.
Homework Practice Masters	Additional practice in computational and spiral review exercises for each lesson in the Student Edition. These masters are included in the Chapter Resource Masters.
Reteach and Skills Practice Workbook	A consumable version of the Reteach and Skills Masters for each lesson.
Homework Practice Workbook	A consumable version of the Homework Practice Masters for each lesson.
Problem Solving Workbook	A consumable version of the Problem Solving Masters for each lesson.

Technology Products

ExamView® Assessment Suite	Networkable software includes a Worksheet Builder to make worksheets and tests, a Student Module to take tests on-screen, and a Management System to keep student records.
Math Adventures with Dot and Ray	Provides entertaining activities and math games that use a problem-solving format.
Math Songs	Collections of songs, raps, and chants that are aligned to the California Standards.
Math Tool Chest	Contains inquiry-based concept building software with interactive representations of manipulatives.

Diagnostic and Placement
Grade K

Name _____

Date _____

This test contains 15 questions. Work each problem in the space on this page. Select the best answer. Write the answer as directed.

1 Count the apples. Write the number. _____

2 Put an X on the set of four cherries.

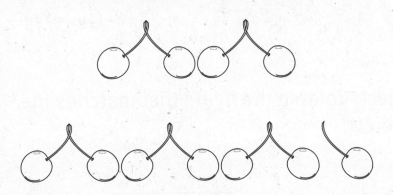

3 Circle the problem that fits the story.

 $\begin{array}{r} 2 \\ -\ 1 \\ \hline 1 \end{array}$ $\begin{array}{r} 2 \\ +\ 1 \\ \hline 3 \end{array}$

4 Look at the first square. Circle the squares that are the same size.

5 Circle the shape that comes next.

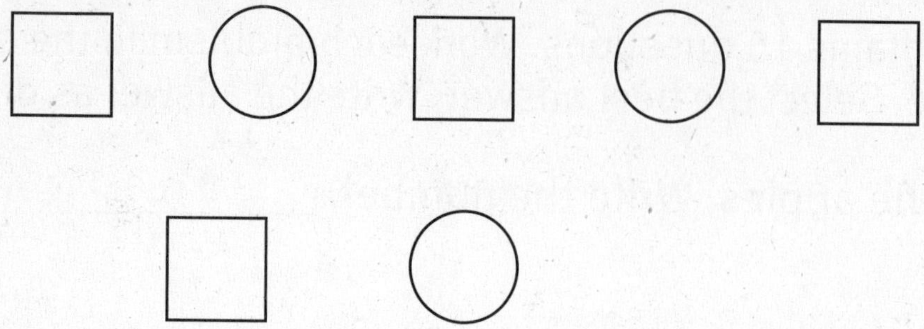

6 Look at the pattern. Circle the part that repeats.

7 Look at the object. Color in the figure that matches the shape of the object.

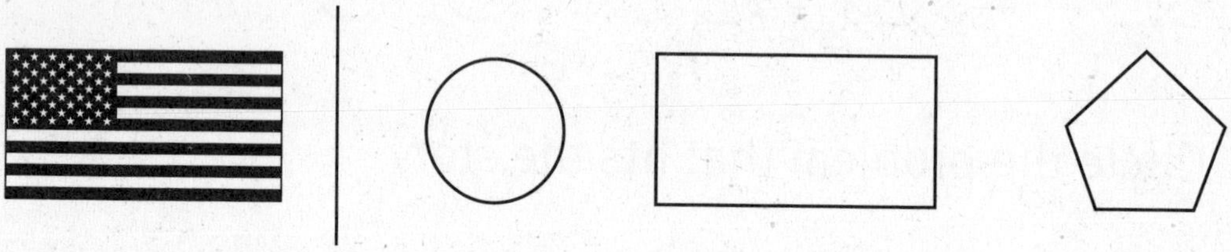

8 Put an X on the objects that can stack.

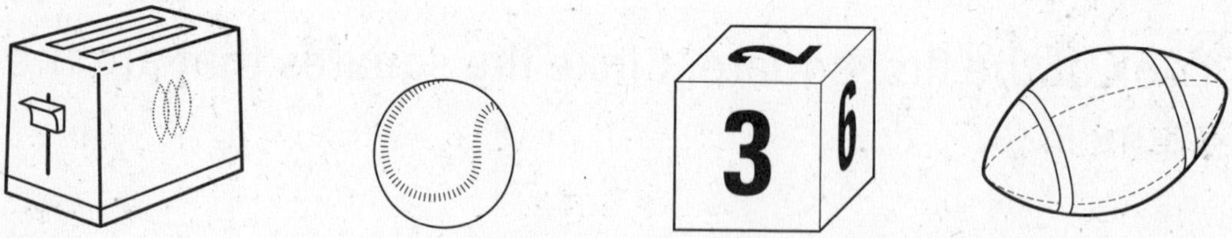

9 Put an X on the sailboat that is in the middle.

10 Put an X on the crayon that is under the table.

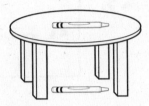

11 Put an X on the object that is next to the tree.

12 Circle the shorter object.

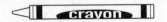   

13 Circle the object that holds more.

14 Sort the crayons by color. Use tally marks to show how many crayons are in each group.

Number of Crayons	
Crayons	Tally
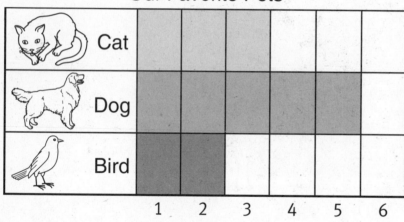	

15 Look at the group. Write how many of each pet.

Our Favorite Pets

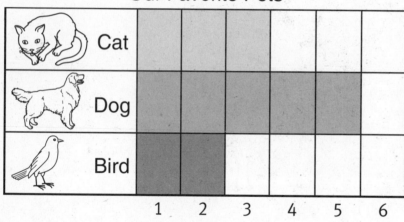

_____   _____   _____

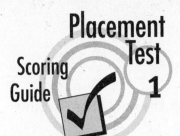

Placement Test 1

Scoring Guide

For each part, mark the box under the number of correctly answered questions.

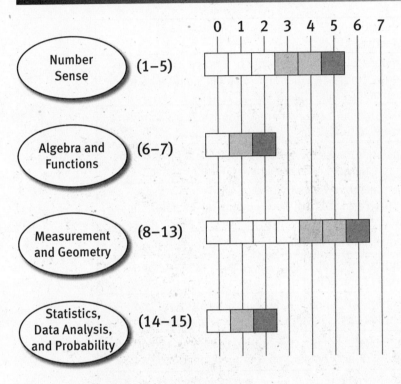

Mark the total number correct below.

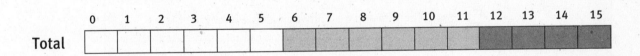

Total

Key: Consider this student for...

☐ *Math Triumphs*

▨ Grade 1 Strategic Intervention—See page 12 for materials list.

▮ Grade 1

Placement Test 1

Learning Objectives

Student Name _____

In the column on the left, mark the questions that the student answered *incorrectly*.

Strand	May Need Intervention	Objective
Number Sense	☐ 1	compare two or more sets of objects (up to 10 objects in each group) and identify which set is equal to, more than, or less than the other
	☐ 2	count, recognize, represent, name, and order a number of objects (up to 30)
	☐ 3	know that the larger numbers describe sets with more objects in them than the smaller numbers have
	☐ 4	use concrete objects to determine the answers to addition and subtraction problems (for two numbers that are each less than 10)
	☐ 5	recognize when an estimate is reasonable
Algebra and Functions	☐ 6	identify, sort, and classify objects by attribute and identify objects that do not belong to a particular group
	☐ 7	identify, sort, and classify objects by attribute and identify objects that do not belong to a particular group
Measurement and Geometry	☐ 8	compare the length, weight, and capacity of objects by making direct comparisons with reference objects
	☐ 9	compare the length, weight, and capacity of objects by making direct comparisons with reference objects
	☐ 10	name the days of the week
	☐ 11	identify the time (to the nearest hour) of everyday events
	☐ 12	identify and describe common geometric objects
	☐ 13	compare familiar plane and solid objects by common attributes
Statistics, Data Analysis, and Probability	☐ 14	pose information questions; collect data; and record the results using objects, pictures, and picture graphs
	☐ 15	identify, describe, and extend simple patterns (such as circles or triangles) by referring to their shapes, sizes, or colors

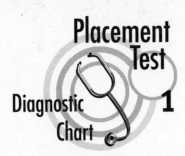

Placement Test 1

Diagnostic Chart

Student Performance Level	Number of Questions Correct	Suggestions for Intervention and Remediation
Intensive Intervention	**0–5**	Use *California Math Triumphs* to accelerate the achievement of students who are two or more years below grade level. Students should follow a personalized remediation plan. A variety of materials and instructional methods are recommended. For example, instruction and practice should be provided in print, technology, and hands-on lessons.
Strategic Intervention	**6–11**	Use the additional Intervention and Remediation materials listed on the next page. This list of materials can provide helpful resources for students who struggle in the traditional mathematics program. Strategic intervention allows students to continue to remain in the *California Mathematics: Concepts, Skills, and Problem Solving* program, while receiving the differentiated instruction they need. Teaching Tips and other resources are also listed in the Teacher Wraparound Edition.
Grade 1	**12 or more**	Use *California Mathematics: Concepts, Skills, and Problem Solving*. This student does not require overall intervention. However, based on the student's performance on the different sections, intervention may be required. For example, a student who missed 4 or more questions in the Measurement and Geometry section may require extra assistance as you cover these skills throughout the year.

A Special Note About Intervention

When using diagnostic tests, teachers should always question the reason behind the students' scores. Students can struggle with mathematics concepts for a variety of reasons. Personalized instruction is recommended for English language learners, students with specific learning disabilities, students with certain medical conditions, or for those who struggle with traditional instructional practice. Teachers should always consider the needs of the individual student when determining the best approach for instruction and program placement.

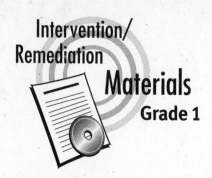

Intervention/ Remediation Materials
Grade 1

Print Materials

Reteach Masters	A brief explanation, along with examples and exercises, for every lesson in the Student Edition. These masters are included in the Chapter Resource Masters.
Skills Practice Masters	Additional practice in computational and application exercises for each lesson in the Student Edition. These masters are included in the Chapter Resource Masters.
Homework Practice Masters	Additional practice in computational and spiral review exercises for each lesson in the Student Edition. These masters are included in the Chapter Resource Masters.
Reteach and Skills Practice Workbook	A consumable version of the Reteach and Skills Masters for each lesson.
Homework Practice Workbook	A consumable version of the Homework Practice Masters for each lesson.
Problem Solving Workbook	A consumable version of the Problem Solving Masters for each lesson.

Technology Products

ExamView® Assessment Suite	Networkable software includes a Worksheet Builder to make worksheets and tests, a Student Module to take tests on-screen, and a Management System to keep student records.
Math Adventures with Dot and Ray	Provides entertaining activities and math games that use a problem-solving format.
Math Songs	Collections of songs, raps, and chants that are aligned to the California Standards.
Math Tool Chest	Contains inquiry-based concept building software with interactive representations of manipulatives.

**Diagnostic and Placement
Grade 1**

Name _____

Date _____

This test contains 15 questions. Work each problem in the space on this page. Select the best answer. Circle the correct answer.

1 Which animal do you see most of in the picture?

2 How many apples are in the picture?

25   26   27   28

3 How many objects are in the larger set?

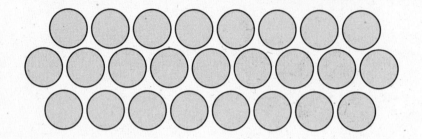

     14   15   25   26

4 How many are left?

   2   4   5   6

5 About how many?

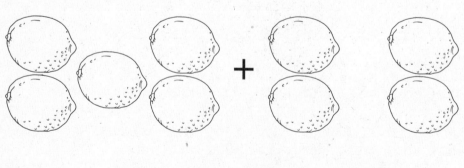

   5   10   15   20

6 Which object does not belong?

   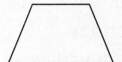

7 Which object does not belong?

8 Which holds more?

9 Which is the heaviest?

California Diagnostic and Placement Tests

10 Which is the next day after Tuesday?

Sunday
Monday
Wednesday
Thursday

11 What time did Rosario go to bed?

4:00   12:00   8:00   2:00

12 Which is a circle?

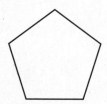

13 Which object does not belong?

14 Which set of shapes matches the picture graph?

Favorite Shapes					
◯ Circle	◯	◯	◯		
△ Triangle	△	△	△	△	

△◯△◯△

◯△◯△◯△◯

△◯△◯△◯△◯△

△◯◯△◯△◯

15 Which pattern matches?

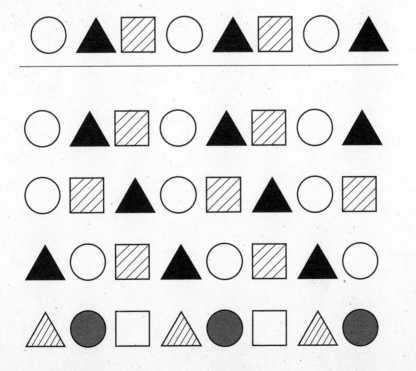

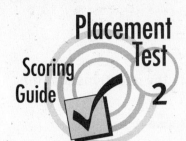

Placement
Scoring Test
Guide 2

For each part, mark the box under the number of correctly answered questions.

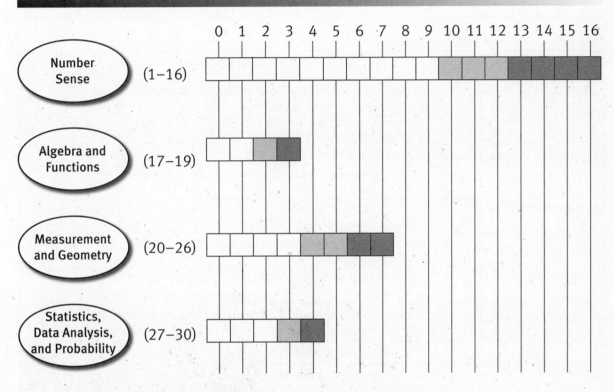

Number Sense (1–16)

Algebra and Functions (17–19)

Measurement and Geometry (20–26)

Statistics, Data Analysis, and Probability (27–30)

Mark the total number correct below.

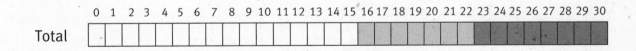

Total

Key: Consider this student for...

☐ *Math Triumphs*

▨ Grade 2 Strategic Intervention—See page 22 for materials list.

▨ Grade 2

Placement Test 2
Learning Objectives

Student Name _____

In the column on the left, mark the questions that the student answered *incorrectly*.

Strand	May Need Intervention	Objective
Number Sense	☐ 1	count, read, and write whole numbers to 100
	☐ 2 ☐ 3 ☐ 4	compare and order whole numbers to 100 by using the symbols for less than, equal to, or greater than ($<,=,>$)
	☐ 5	count and group objects in ones and tens
	☐ 6	count by 2's, 5's, and 10's to 100
	☐ 7	identify and know the value of coins and show different combinations of coins that equal the same value
	☐ 8	know the addition facts (sums to 20) and the corresponding subtraction facts and commit them to memory
	☐ 9 ☐ 10	use the inverse relationship between addition and subtraction to solve problems
	☐ 11 ☐ 12	identify one more than, one less than, 10 more than, and 10 less than a given number
	☐ 13 ☐ 14	show the meaning of addition (putting together, increasing) and subtraction (taking away, comparing, finding the difference)
	☐ 15	solve addition and subtraction problems with one- and two-digit numbers
Algebra and Functions	☐ 16	represent equivalent forms of the same number through the use of physical models, diagrams, and number expressions (to 20)
	☐ 17	write and solve number sentences from problem situations that express relationships involving addition and subtraction
	☐ 18	understand the meaning of the symbols $+, -, =$
	☐ 19	create problem situations that might lead to given number sentences Content involving addition and subtraction
Measurement and Geometry	☐ 20	compare the length, weight, and volume of two or more objects by using direct comparison or a nonstandard unit
	☐ 21	tell time to the nearest half hour and relate time to events
	☐ 22 ☐ 23	identify, describe, and compare triangles, rectangles, squares, and circles, including the faces of three-dimensional objects
	☐ 24	classify familiar plane and solid objects by common attributes and explain which attributes are being used for classification
	☐ 25	give and follow directions about location
	☐ 26	arrange and describe objects in space by proximity, position, and direction
Statistics, Data Analysis, and Probability	☐ 27	sort objects and data by common attributes and describe the categories
	☐ 28	represent and compare data by using pictures, bar graphs, tally charts, and picture graphs
	☐ 29 ☐ 30	describe, extend, and explain ways to get to a next element in simple repeating patterns

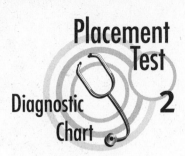

Placement Test
Diagnostic Chart 2

Student Performance Level	Number of Questions Correct	Suggestions for Intervention and Remediation
Intensive Intervention	0–15	Use *California Math Triumphs* to accelerate the achievement of students who are two or more years below grade level. Students should follow a personalized remediation plan. A variety of materials and instructional methods are recommended. For example, instruction and practice should be provided in print, technology, and hands-on lessons.
Strategic Intervention	16–22	Use the additional Intervention and Remediation materials listed on the next page. This list of materials can provide helpful resources for students who struggle in the traditional mathematics program. Strategic intervention allows students to continue to remain in the *California Mathematics: Concepts, Skills, and Problem Solving* program, while receiving the differentiated instruction they need. Teaching Tips and other resources are also listed in the Teacher Wraparound Edition.
Grade 2	23 or more	Use *California Mathematics: Concepts, Skills, and Problem Solving*. This student does not require overall intervention. However, based on the student's performance on the different sections, intervention may be required. For example, a student who missed 5 or more questions in the Measurement and Geometry section may require extra assistance as you cover these skills throughout the year.

A Special Note About Intervention

When using diagnostic tests, teachers should always question the reason behind the students' scores. Students can struggle with mathematics concepts for a variety of reasons. Personalized instruction is recommended for English language learners, students with specific learning disabilities, students with certain medical conditions, or for those who struggle with traditional instructional practice. Teachers should always consider the needs of the individual student when determining the best approach for instruction and program placement.

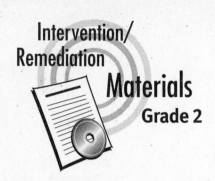

Intervention/Remediation Materials

Grade 2

Print Materials	
Reteach Masters	A brief explanation, along with examples and exercises, for every lesson in the Student Edition. These masters are included in the Chapter Resource Masters.
Skills Practice Masters	Additional practice in computational and application exercises for each lesson in the Student Edition. These masters are included in the Chapter Resource Masters.
Homework Practice Masters	Additional practice in computational and spiral review exercises for each lesson in the Student Edition. These masters are included in the Chapter Resource Masters.
Reteach and Skills Practice Workbook	A consumable version of the Reteach and Skills Masters for each lesson.
Homework Practice Workbook	A consumable version of the Homework Practice Masters for each lesson.
Problem Solving Workbook	A consumable version of the Problem Solving Masters for each lesson.

Technology Products	
ExamView® Assessment Suite	Networkable software includes a Worksheet Builder to make worksheets and tests, a Student Module to take tests on-screen, and a Management System to keep student records.
Math Adventures with Dot and Ray	Provides entertaining activities and math games that use a problem-solving format.
Math Songs	Collections of songs, raps, and chants that are aligned to the California Standards.
Math Tool Chest	Contains inquiry-based concept building software with interactive representations of manipulatives.

Name _____

Date _____

This test contains 30 questions. Work each problem in the space on this page. Circle the best answer.

1 What number is shown by the blocks?

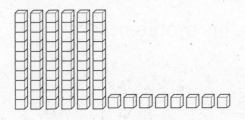

14   60   68   86

2 Which sign makes the number sentence 43 ◯ 34 true?

=   +   >   <

3 Which number is between 68 and 70?   68, ___, 70

67   69   71   72

4 What sign makes the number sentence true? 10 ☐ 6 = 16

+   −   ×   =

5 What number has 3 ones and 4 tens?

34   43   304   403

6 What is the missing number?   30, 32, 34, __, 38, 40, 42

33   35   36   37

7 How much money is shown?

| 39¢ | 34¢ | 29¢ | 24¢ |

8 What is the solution to this problem?

$$\begin{array}{r} 13 \\ +4 \\ \hline \end{array}$$

| 8 | 9 | 17 | 18 |

9 Which of these can be used to check the answers to the problem below? $5 + 7 = 12$

$7 + 12 = 19$ $4 + 8 = 12$
$17 - 5 = 12$ $12 - 7 = 5$

10 Which of these can be used to check the answers to the problem below? $9 - 6 = 3$

$3 + 6 = 9$ $9 + 6 = 15$
$6 - 3 = 3$ $12 - 3 = 9$

11 What number is 10 less than 70?

| 60 | 69 | 71 | 80 |

12 What number is 1 more than 53?

| 43 | 52 | 54 | 63 |

13 Which number sentence tells how many in all?

$$8 + 6 = 14$$
$$4 + 3 = 7$$

$$8 - 6 = 2$$
$$4 - 3 = 1$$

14 Which number sentence tells how many more triangles than squares?

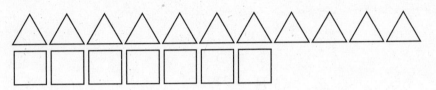

$$11 - 7 =$$
$$11 - 4 =$$

$$7 + 11 =$$
$$7 - 11 =$$

15 What is the solution to the problem?

$$\begin{array}{r} 26 \\ +6 \\ \hline \end{array}$$

14   21   22   32

16 What number makes the number sentence true?
$$3 + 6 = \square + 5$$

3   4   5   6

17 About how many linking cubes can you hold in one hand?

About 5   About 500

About 50   About 5,000

18 There are 6 baseballs. Eric tossed 2 of them. Which number sentence shows how many are left?

$6 - 2 = 4$ $6 - 4 = 2$
$2 + 6 = 8$ $2 + 4 = 6$

19 Which number sentence matches the picture?

$5 + 3 =$ $5 - 3 =$
$8 + 3 =$ $8 - 3 =$

20 Circle the longest object.

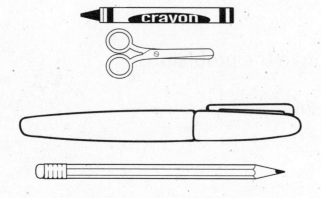

21 What time is shown on the clock?

2:30   3:30   6:15   7:15

22 Which shape is a triangle?

23 Which of the figures has 4 corners and 4 sides?

24 Which solid figure has a face that is a circle?

25 Begin on start. Go down 1. Go right 2. Circle where you are.

Start		

26 Which object is to the left of the boat?

27 Which tally table shows how many triangles, squares, and circles?

28 How many more chose bananas than apples?

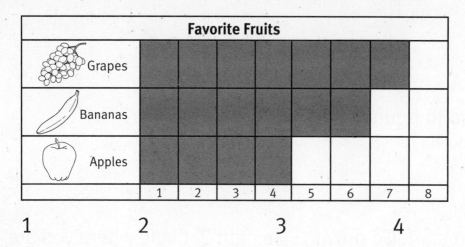

Favorite Fruits								
Grapes								
Bananas								
Apples								
	1	2	3	4	5	6	7	8

1   2   3   4

29 Which part of the pattern repeats?

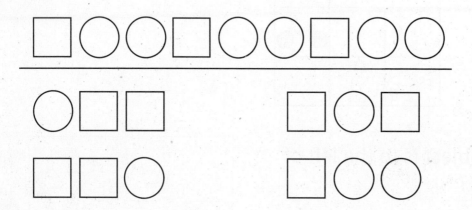

30 Which two show the same pattern? Circle them.

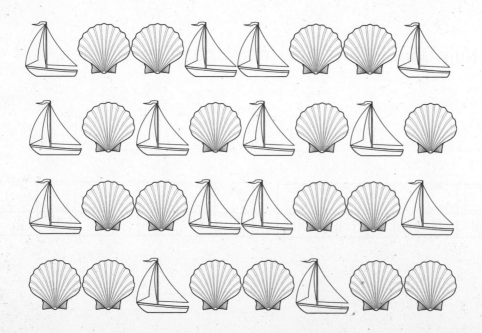

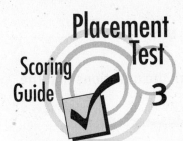
Student Name _____

For each part, mark the box under the number of correctly answered questions.

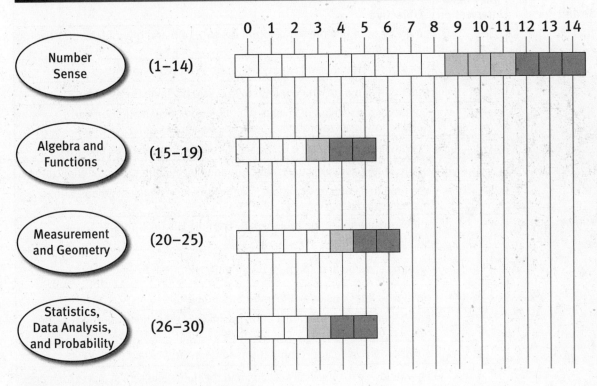

		0 1 2 3 4 5 6 7 8 9 10 11 12 13 14
Number Sense	(1–14)	
Algebra and Functions	(15–19)	
Measurement and Geometry	(20–25)	
Statistics, Data Analysis, and Probability	(26–30)	

Mark the total number correct below.

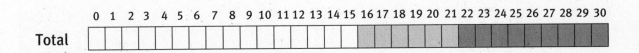

Total   0 1 2 3 4 5 6 7 8 9 10 11 12 13 14 15 16 17 18 19 20 21 22 23 24 25 26 27 28 29 30

Key: Consider this student for...

☐ *Math Triumphs*

▨ Grade 3 Strategic Intervention—See page 32 for materials list.

▨ Grade 3

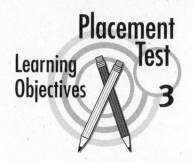

Placement Test 3
Learning Objectives

Student Name _____

In the column on the left, mark the questions that the student answered *incorrectly*.

Strand	May Need Intervention	Objective
Number Sense	☐ 1	count, read, and write whole numbers to 1,000 and identify the place value for each digit
	☐ 2	use words, models, and expanded forms to represent numbers
	☐ 3	order and compare whole numbers to 1,000 by using the symbols $<, =, >$
	☐ 4	understand and use the inverse relationship between addition and subtraction to solve problems and check solutions
	☐ 5	find the sum or difference of two whole numbers up to three digits long
	☐ 6	use repeated addition, arrays, and counting by multiples to do multiplication
	☐ 7	use repeated subtraction, equal sharing, and forming equal groups with remainders to do division
	☐ 8	know the multiplication tables of 2s, 5s, and 10s (to "times 10") and commit them to memory
	☐ 9 ☐ 10	recognize, name and compare unit fractions from $\frac{1}{12}$ to $\frac{1}{2}$
	☐ 11	recognize fractions of whole and parts of a group
	☐ 12	know that when all fractional parts are included, such as four-fourths, the result is equal to the whole and to one
	☐ 13	solve problems using combinations of coins and bills
	☐ 14	know and use the decimal notation and the dollar and cent symbols for money
	☐ 15	solve addition and subtraction problems by using data from simple charts, picture graphs, and number sentences
Algebra and Functions	☐ 16 ☐ 17	use the commulative and associative rules to simplify mental calculations and to check results
	☐ 18 ☐ 19	relate problem situations to number sentences involving addition and subtraction
Measurement and Geometry	☐ 20 ☐ 21	measure the length of an object to the nearest inch and/or centimeter
	☐ 22	tell time to the nearest quarter hour and know relationships of time
	☐ 23	determine the duration of intervals of time in hours
	☐ 24	decribe and classify plane and solid geometric shapes according to the number and shape of faces, edges, and vertices
	☐ 25	put shapes together and take them apart to form other shapes
	☐ 26	recognize, describe, and extend patterns and determine a next term in linear patterns
Statistics, Data Analysis, and Probability	☐ 27 ☐ 28	represent the same data set in more than one way
	☐ 29	identify features of data set (range and mode)
	☐ 30	recognize, describe, and extend patterns and determine a next term in linear patterns

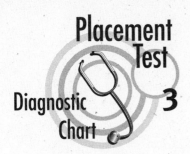

Placement Test
Diagnostic Chart
3

Student Performance Level	Number of Questions Correct	Suggestions for Intervention and Remediation
Intensive Intervention	0–15	Use *California Math Triumphs* to accelerate the achievement of students who are two or more years below grade level. Students should follow a personalized remediation plan. A variety of materials and instructional methods are recommended. For example, instruction and practice should be provided in print, technology, and hands-on lessons.
Strategic Intervention	16–22	Use the additional Intervention and Remediation materials listed on the next page. This list of materials can provide helpful resources for students who struggle in the traditional mathematics program. Strategic intervention allows students to continue to remain in the *California Mathematics: Concepts, Skills, and Problem Solving* program, while receiving the differentiated instruction they need. Teaching Tips and other resources are also listed in the Teacher Wraparound Edition.
Grade 3	23 or more	Use *California Mathematics: Concepts, Skills, and Problem Solving*. This student does not require overall intervention. However, based on the student's performance on the different sections, intervention may be required. For example, a student who missed 4 or more questions in the Measurement and Geometry section may require extra assistance as you cover these skills throughout the year.

A Special Note About Intervention

When using diagnostic tests, teachers should always question the reason behind the students' scores. Students can struggle with mathematics concepts for a variety of reasons. Personalized instruction is recommended for English language learners, students with specific learning disabilities, students with certain medical conditions, or for those who struggle with traditional instructional practice. Teachers should always consider the needs of the individual student when determining the best approach for instruction and program placement.

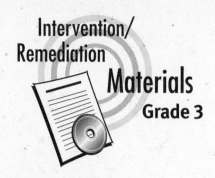

Intervention/ Remediation Materials
Grade 3

Print Materials

Reteach Masters	A brief explanation, along with examples and exercises, for every lesson in the Student Edition. (Two pages for Problem-Solving Lessons and one page per lesson for all other lessons.) These masters are included in the Chapter Resource Masters.
Skills Practice Masters	Additional practice in computational and application exercises for each lesson in the Student Edition. These masters are included in the Chapter Resource Masters.
Homework Practice Masters	Additional practice in computational and spiral review exercises for each lesson in the Student Edition. These masters are included in the Chapter Resource Masters.
Study Guide and Intervention Workbook	A consumable version of the Study Guide and Intervention Masters for each lesson. Also available in Spanish.
Skills Practice Workbook	A consumable version of the Skills Practice Workbook Masters for each lesson. Also available in Spanish.
Practice Workbook	A consumable version of the Practice Masters for each lesson. Also available in Spanish.
Prerequisite Skills Workbook	Arithmetic study guide and practice pages for each of the prerequisite skills that review basic math concepts.

Technology Products

ExamView® Assessment Suite	Networkable software includes a Worksheet Builder to make worksheets and tests, a Student Module to take tests on-screen, and a Management System to keep student records.
Math Adventures with Dot and Ray	Provides entertaining activities and math games that use a problem-solving format.
Math Songs	Collections of songs, raps, and chants that are aligned to the California Standards.
Math Tool Chest	Contains inquiry-based concept building software with interactive representations of manipulatives.

Diagnostic and Placement Grade 3

Name _____

Date _____

This test contains 30 multiple-choice questions. Work each problem in the space on this page. Select the best answer. Write the letter of the answer on the blank at the right.

1 A number has three ones, two tens, and seven hundreds. What is the number?

    A 273   **B** 327   **C** 723   **D** 732

1 _____

2 What is another way to write five hundred sixty-four?

    F $500 + 6 + 4$ **H** $500 + 60 + 4$
    G $5 + 6 + 4$ **J** $560 + 40$

2 _____

3 Which number sentence is true?

    A $625 < 671$ **C** $625 < 625$
    B $625 > 641$ **D** $625 > 714$

3 _____

4 Juan did this addition problem. Which problem shows he got the right answer? $6 + 2 = 8$

    F $3 + 5 = 8$ **H** $6 - 2 = 4$
    G $8 + 2 = 10$ **J** $8 - 2 = 6$

4 _____

5
$$\begin{array}{r} 244 \\ + 38 \\ \hline \end{array}$$

    A 372   **B** 282   **C** 272   **D** 216

5 _____

6 Which drawing shows 6×4?

    F   **G**   **H**   **J**

6 _____

7 Which of the following fractions is the least?

    A $\frac{1}{2}$ **B** $\frac{1}{4}$ **C** $\frac{1}{9}$ **D** $\frac{1}{12}$

7 _____

8 There are eight tables at the restaurant. There are two chairs at each table. How many chairs are there altogether?

8   2

F 10   **G** 16   **H** 24   **J** 28

8 _____

9 Nina has these crayons. She will put six crayons in each of three boxes. How many crayons will be left out of the boxes?

A 1   **B** 2   **C** 3   **D** 4

9 _____

10 Which of the following fractions is the greatest?

F $\frac{1}{3}$ **G** $\frac{1}{4}$ **H** $\frac{1}{8}$ **J** $\frac{1}{10}$

10 _____

11 Which fraction is equal to one whole?

A $\frac{5}{5}$ **B** $\frac{2}{3}$ **C** $\frac{3}{8}$ **D** $\frac{1}{4}$

11 _____

12 What fraction of the group of animals is cows?

F $\frac{5}{2}$ **G** $\frac{2}{3}$ **H** $\frac{3}{5}$ **J** $\frac{2}{5}$

12 _____

13 Tyler has three quarters, five dimes, and one nickel in his piggy bank. How much money does he have?

A $1.10   **B** $1.25   **C** $1.30   **D** $1.60

13 _____

14 What is another way to write fifty-two cents?

52¢

F $52   **G** 52$ **H** $50.2   **J** $0.52

15 Look at the graph. How many books did they read altogether?

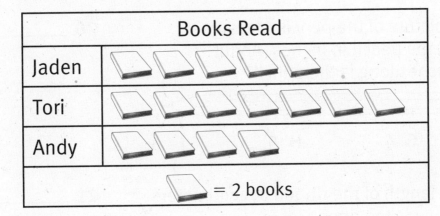

Books Read	
Jaden	📖📖📖📖📖
Tori	📖📖📖📖📖📖📖
Andy	📖📖📖📖
📖 = 2 books	

A 11   **B** 12   **C** 16   **D** 32

16 What number goes in the box to make this number sentence true?

$$18 + 6 = \boxed{} + 18$$

F 6   **G** 12   **H** 18   **J** 24

17 Look at the addition problem in the box. Which problem below has the same answer?

$$\boxed{7 + 4 + 5 = 16}$$

A 16 + 5 + 4 =   **C** 6 + 3 + 4 =
B 7 + 4 + 16 =   **D** 5 + 7 + 4 =

18 Ellie had 26 stickers. Rick gave her some stickers. Now she has 41. Which number sentence could be used to find how many stickers Rick gave Ellie?

F $\boxed{} - 41 = 26$ **H** $\boxed{} + 41 = 26$
G $26 - \boxed{} = 41$ **J** $26 + \boxed{} = 41$

19 There are 213 third graders and 251 fourth
graders. Which number sentence can be used
to find how many more fourth graders there are
than third graders?

19 _____

A $213 - 251 = \Box$ **C** $251 - 213 = \Box$
B $213 + 251 = \Box$ **D** $251 + 213 = \Box$

20 Look at the picture of the pencil. Measure
the length of the pencil in inches. About
how many inches long is the pencil?

20 _____

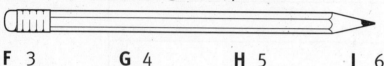

F 3   **G** 4   **H** 5   **J** 6

21 Measure the length of the ribbon in centimeters.
About how long is the ribbon?

21 _____

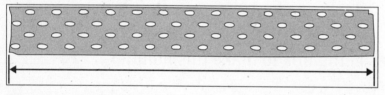

A 8 centimeters   **C** 10 centimeters
B 9 centimeters   **D** 11 centimeters

22 Peter has basketball practice one time every
week. How many times does he have basketball
practice in one year?

22 _____

F 24   **G** 52   **H** 60   **J** 365

23 A movie started at 6:00 P.M. and lasted two
hours. When did the movie end?

23 _____

A 4:00 P.M.   **B** 7:00 P.M.   **C** 8:00 P.M.   **D** 9:00 P.M.

24 How many faces does this pyramid have?

24 _____

F 8   **G** 5   **H** 4   **J** 3

25 Look at the two triangles. Which of the following shapes could be made from the two triangles? **25** ________

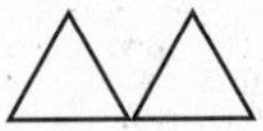

A  **B**  **C** 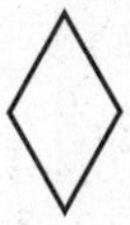 **D** 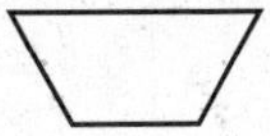

26 One starfish has five arms, two have ten arms, and three have fifteen arms. How many arms do four starfish have? **26** ________

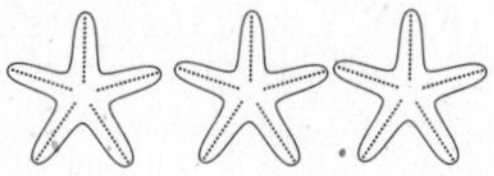

F 15 **G** 20 **H** 25 **J** 30

27 The tally chart shows the number of stars each student earned. Which graph matches the data in the tally chart? **27** ________

Stars Earned	
Name	Tally
Nick	𝍷𝍷𝍷
Grace	𝍸
Faith	𝍷𝍷𝍷𝍷
Ben	𝍸 𝍷

A

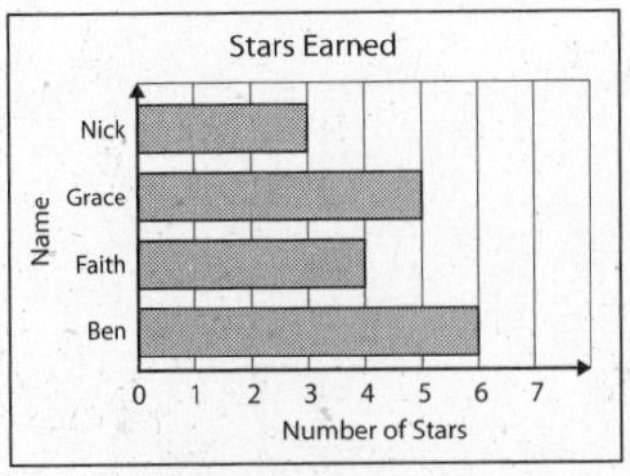
Stars Earned
Nick
Grace
Faith
Ben
Name
0 1 2 3 4 5 6 7
Number of Stars

C

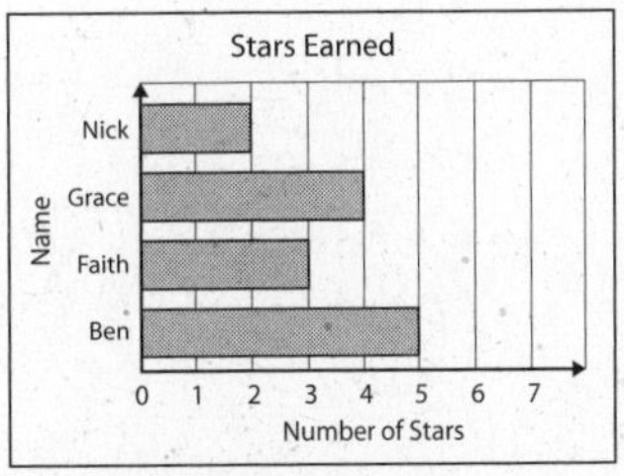
Stars Earned
Nick
Grace
Faith
Ben
Name
0 1 2 3 4 5 6 7
Number of Stars

B

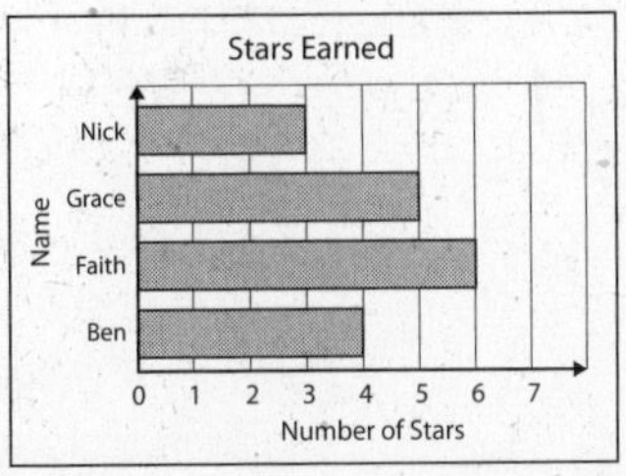
Stars Earned
Nick
Grace
Faith
Ben
Name
0 1 2 3 4 5 6 7
Number of Stars

D

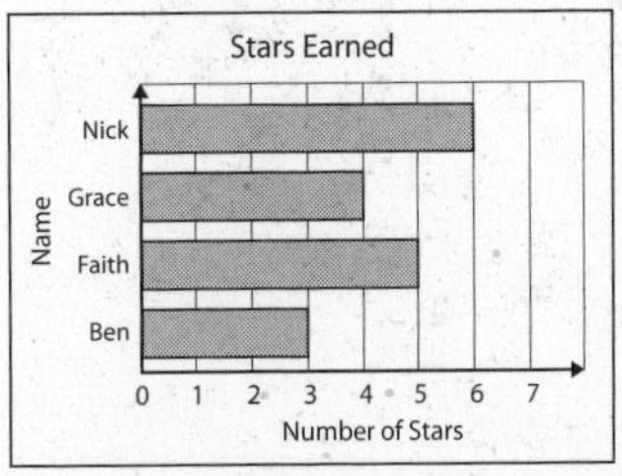
Stars Earned
Nick
Grace
Faith
Ben
Name
0 1 2 3 4 5 6 7
Number of Stars

28 The bar graph shows the number of students who voted for each color. Which tally chart matches the data in the bar graph?

28 _____

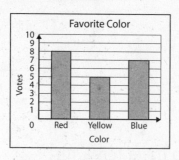

F

Favorite Color	
Red	卌
Yellow	卌 |||
Blue	卌 ||

G

Favorite Color	
Red	卌 |||
Yellow	卌
Blue	卌 ||

H

Favorite Color	
Red	卌 |||
Yellow	卌	
Blue	||||

J

Favorite Color	
Red	卌 |||
Yellow	||||
Blue	卌

29 Which age occurs most often?

29 _____

Students Ages	
Student	Age
Jenny	8
Mandy	10
Eddie	8
Carlos	7
Ross	10
Vicky	8

A 3   **B** 7   **C** 8   **D** 10

30 Five tricycles have fifteen wheels, four have twelve wheels, and three have nine wheels. How many wheels do two tricycles have?

30 _____

F 18   **G** 15   **H** 6   **J** 3

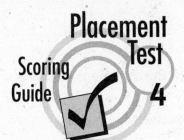

Placement Test 4
Scoring Guide

Student Name _____

For each part, mark the box under the number of correctly answered questions.

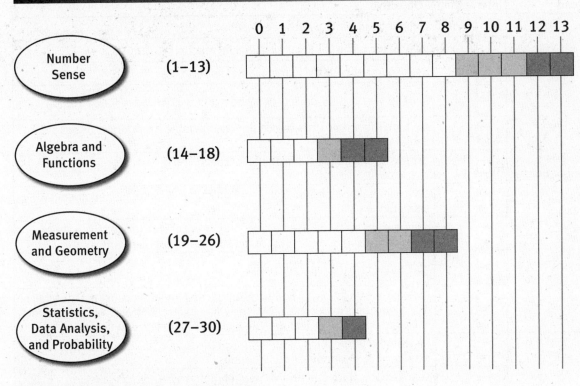

Number Sense (1–13)

Algebra and Functions (14–18)

Measurement and Geometry (19–26)

Statistics, Data Analysis, and Probability (27–30)

Mark the total number correct below.

Total
0 1 2 3 4 5 6 7 8 9 10 11 12 13 14 15 16 17 18 19 20 21 22 23 24 25 26 27 28 29 30

Key: Consider this student for...

☐ *California Math Triumphs*

▨ Grade 4 Strategic Intervention—See page 42 for materials list.

▩ Grade 4

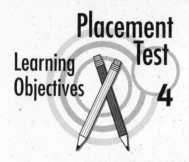

Placement Test 4

Learning Objectives

In the column on the left, mark the questions that the student answered *incorrectly*.

Strand	May Need Intervention	Objective
Number Sense	☐ 1	compare and order whole numbers to 10,000
	☐ 2	identify the place value for each digit in numbers to 10,000
	☐ 3	use expanded notation to represent numbers
	☐ 4 ☐ 5	find the sum or difference of two whole numbers between 0 and 10,000
	☐ 6	memorize to automaticity the multiplication table for numbers between 1 and 10
	☐ 7	use the inverse relationship of multiplication and division to compute and check results
	☐ 8	solve simple problems involving multiplication of multi-digit numbers by one-digit numbers
	☐ 9	compare fractions represented by drawing or concrete materials to show equivalency and to add and subtract simple fractions in context
	☐ 10 ☐ 11	add and subtract simple fractions
	☐ 12 ☐ 13	solve problems involving addition, subtraction, multiplication, and division of money amounts in decimal notation and multiply and divide money amounts in decimal notation by using whole-number multipliers and divisors
Algebra and Functions	☐ 14	represent relationships of quantities in the form of mathematical expressions, equations, or inequalities.
	☐ 15	select appropriate operational and relational symbols to make an expression true
	☐ 16	recognize and use the commutative and associative properties of multiplication
	☐ 17	extend and recognize a linear pattern by its rules
	☐ 18	solve simple problems involving a functional relationship between two quantities
Measurement and Geometry	☐ 19	estimate or determine the area and volume of solid figures by covering them with squares or by counting the number of cubes that would fill them
	☐ 20	find the perimeter of a polygon with interger sides
	☐ 21	choose the appropriate tools and units and estimate and measure the length, liquid volume, and weight/mass of given objects
	☐ 22	identify, describe, classify polygons
	☐ 23	identify attributes of triangles
	☐ 24	identify attributes of quadrilaterals
	☐ 25	identify right angles in geometric figures or in appropriate objects and determine whether others angles are greater or less than a right angle
	☐ 26	identify, describe, and classify common three-dimensional geometric objects
Statistics, Data Analysis, and Probability	☐ 27 ☐ 28	record the possible outcomes for a single event
	☐ 29 ☐ 30	summarize and display the results of probability experiments

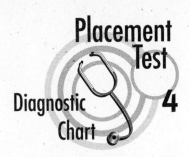

Placement Test 4

Diagnostic Chart

Student Performance Level	Number of Questions Correct	Suggestions for Intervention and Remediation
Intensive Intervention	0–16	Use *California Math Triumphs* to accelerate the achievement of students who are two or more years below grade level. Students should follow a personalized remediation plan. A variety of materials and instructional methods are recommended. For example, instruction and practice should be provided in print, technology, and hands-on lessons.
Strategic Intervention	17–23	Use the additional Intervention and Remediation materials listed on the next page. This list of materials can provide helpful resources for students who struggle in the traditional mathematics program. Strategic intervention allows students to continue to remain in the *California Mathematics: Concepts, Skills, and Problem Solving* program, while receiving the differentiated instruction they need. Teaching Tips and other resources are also listed in the Teacher Wraparound Edition.
Grade 4	24 or more	Use *California Mathematics: Concepts, Skills, and Problem Solving*. This student does not require overall intervention. However, based on the student's performance on the different sections, intervention may be required. For example, a student who missed 5 or more questions in the Measurement and Geometry section may require extra assistance as you cover these skills throughout the year.

A Special Note About Intervention

When using diagnostic tests, teachers should always question the reason behind the students' scores. Students can struggle with mathematics concepts for a variety of reasons. Personalized instruction is recommended for English language learners, students with specific learning disabilities, students with certain medical conditions, or for those who struggle with traditional instructional practice. Teachers should always consider the needs of the individual student when determining the best approach for instruction and program placement.

Intervention/ Remediation Materials
Grade 4

Print Materials

Reteach Masters	A brief explanation, along with examples and exercises, for every lesson in the Student Edition. (Two pages for Problem-Solving Lessons and one page per lesson for all other lessons.) These masters are included in the Chapter Resource Masters.
Skills Practice Masters	Additional practice in computational and application exercises for each lesson in the Student Edition. These masters are included in the Chapter Resource Masters.
Homework Practice Masters	Additional practice in computational and spiral review exercises for each lesson in the Student Edition. These masters are included in the Chapter Resource Masters.
Study Guide and Intervention Workbook	A consumable version of the Study Guide and Intervention Masters for each lesson. Also available in Spanish.
Skills Practice Workbook	A consumable version of the Skills Practice Workbook Masters for each lesson. Also available in Spanish.
Practice Workbook	A consumable version of the Practice Masters for each lesson. Also available in Spanish.
Prerequisite Skills Workbook	Arithmetic study guide and practice pages for each of the prerequisite skills that review basic math concepts.

Technology Products

ExamView® Assessment Suite	Networkable software includes a Worksheet Builder to make worksheets and tests, a Student Module to take tests on-screen, and a Management System to keep student records.
Math Adventures with Dot and Ray	Provides entertaining activities and math games that use a problem-solving format.
Math Songs	Collections of songs, raps, and chants that are aligned to the California Standards.
Math Tool Chest	Contains inquiry-based concept building software with interactive representations of manipulatives.

Diagnostic and Placement Grade 4

Name _____

Date _____

This test contains 30 multiple-choice questions. Work each problem in the space on this page. Select the best answer. Write the letter of the answer on the blank at the right.

1 Which set of numbers is in order from least to greatest?

    A 895, 924, 862, 941

    B 862, 895, 924, 941

    C 924, 941, 862, 895

    D 941, 924, 895, 862

1 _____

2 Which number has a 7 in the ones place and a 2 in the hundreds place?

    F 2437   **G** 3274   **H** 4237   **J** 4732

2 _____

3 The school auditorium seats 2870 people. Which of these equals 2870?

    A 2 + 8 + 70

    B 200 + 80 + 7

    C 2000 + 800 + 70

    D 2000 + 800 + 7

3 _____

4 5718 + 605 =

    F 5313   **G** 5323   **H** 6313   **J** 6323

4 _____

5 Which number is 16 less than 740?

    A 724   **B** 734   **C** 736   **D** 756

5 _____

6 8 × 3 =

    F 11   **G** 16   **H** 24   **J** 32

6 _____

California Diagnostic and Placement Tests

7 Andrés did the division problem $552 \div 12 = 46$.
Which problem could he do to check his answer?

  A $46 + 12 = \square$ **C** $46 \times 12 = \square$

  B $46 - 12 = \square$ **D** $46 \div 12 = \square$

8 Each student brought in 4 cans of food to donate to the food bank. There are 285 students. How many cans did the students donate in all?

  F 820   **G** 840   **H** 1120   **J** 1140

9 Inali and his friends ate $\frac{1}{2}$ of a pizza.

Which fractional part of a circle below is equal to $\frac{1}{2}$?

  A   **B**   **C**   **D**

10 $\frac{3}{8} + \frac{1}{2} =$

  F $\frac{2}{6}$ **G** $\frac{4}{10}$ **H** $\frac{4}{8}$ **J** $\frac{7}{8}$

11 Desiree drew a rectangle and divided it into 8 equal parts. She colored $\frac{3}{8}$ of the rectangle red, $\frac{2}{8}$ of the rectangle blue, and the rest green. What fraction of the rectangle did Desiree color green?

  A $\frac{1}{8}$ **B** $\frac{3}{8}$ **C** $\frac{5}{8}$ **D** $\frac{6}{8}$

12 Ana bought 3 books and a marker. She paid with a ten-dollar bill. How much change should she get back?

  F $1.45   **G** $5.95   **H** $6.75   **J** $8.55

13 The menu shows the prices at Lunchtime Cafe. Tina ordered a turkey sandwich, salad, and juice. What was the total cost of her meal?

13 _____

Lunchtime Cafe	
Item	**Cost**
Turkey Sandwich	$4.50
Ham Sandwich	$4.35
Salad	$2.10
Fruit Cup	$2.50
Juice	$1.90

A $6.60   **B** $7.50   **C** $8.35   **D** $8.50

14 Drew has 4 sheets of stickers. Each sheet has 12 stickers. Which number sentence shows how to find the total number of stickers Drew has?

14 _____

F $12 + 4 = \square$ **H** $12 \times 4 = \square$

G $12 - 4 = \square$ **J** $12 \div 4 = \square$

15 Which sign goes in the box to make the number sentence true? $36 \square 9 = 27$

15 _____

A +   **B** −   **C** ×   **D** ÷

16 If $15 \times 24 \times 8 = 2880$, then what is $8 \times 24 \times 15$?

16 _____

F 120   **H** 360

G 192   **J** 2880

17 The table shows the number of crayons in each box. If every box has the same number of crayons, how many crayons will be in 8 boxes?

17 _____

Number of Boxes	Number of Crayons
1	8
2	16
3	24

A 8   **B** 32   **C** 64   **D** 72

California Diagnostic and Placement Tests

18 If one dog biscuit costs 45¢, how much will 6 dog biscuits cost?

18 _____

    F $0.51   **G** $2.40   **H** $2.51   **J** $2.70

19 What is the area of this figure?

19 _____

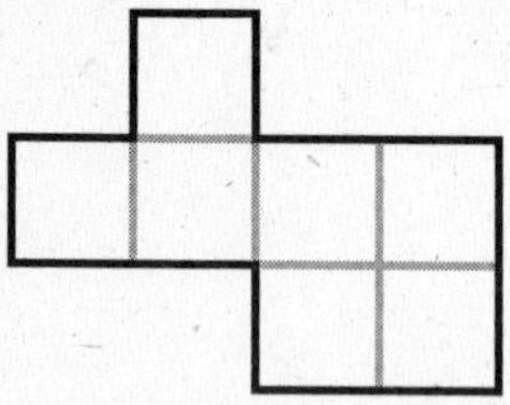

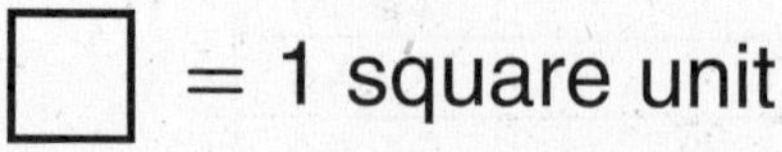

$\square$ = 1 square unit

    A 4 square units   **C** 7 square units
    B 6 square units   **D** 8 square units

20 A classroom is shaped like a rectangle with a length of 30 feet and a width of 24 feet.

20 _____

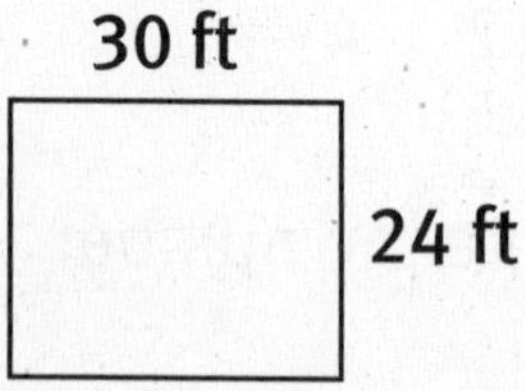

30 ft
24 ft

What is the perimeter in feet of the classroom?

    F 54 feet   **G** 84 feet   **H** 108 feet   **J** 720 feet

21 Which of the following would you measure in feet?

21 _____

    A the length of an eraser
    B the height of a classmate
    C the weight of a book
    D the capacity of a bucket

22 Which best describes this figure?

22 _____

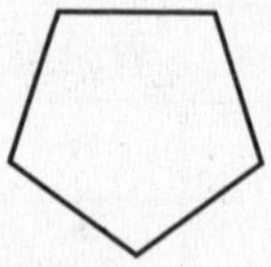

    F pentagon **G** hexagon **H** triangle **J** octagon

23 An equilateral triangle MUST have

    A one angle that is a right angle.

    B no sides that are the same length.

    C all 3 sides that are the same length.

    D only 2 sides that are the same length.

23 _____

24 Which best describes a square?

    F opposite sides equal and 2 right angles

    G parallel sides and no right angles

    H no sides equal and no right angles

    J all sides equal and 4 right angles

24 _____

25 Look at the four angles marked on the picture of a bicycle.

25 _____

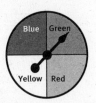

Which angle is a right angle?

    A angle 1   **B** angle 2   **C** angle 3   **D** angle 4

26 Which shape is this can of soup? 🥫 Soup

26 _____

    F sphere   **G** cylinder   **H** cone   **J** pyramid

27 Which table would be best to use to record the outcomes of spinning this spinner?

27 _____

A	Spin Results	
Red	
Purple	
Yellow	
Green	

B	Spin Results	
Red	
Blue	
Yellow	

C	Spin Results	
Red	
Blue	
Yellow	
Green	

D	Spin Results	
Blue	
Yellow	
Green	

California Diagnostic and Placement Tests

28 Ricardo tossed a coin 10 times. It landed heads up 6 times and tails up 4 times. Which tally chart shows these results?

28 _____

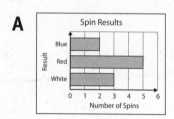

F
Results	
Heads	ᎀᎀᎀᎀ
Tails	||||

G
Results	
Heads	||||
Tails	ᎀᎀᎀᎀ|

H
Results	
Heads	ᎀᎀᎀᎀ
Tails	ᎀᎀᎀᎀ

J
Results	
Heads	ᎀᎀᎀᎀ|
Tails	||

29 Kenji spun a spinner 10 times. The results are shown in the tally chart. Which graph shows these results?

29 _____

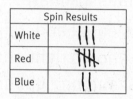

Spin Results	
White	|||
Red	ᎀᎀᎀᎀ
Blue	||

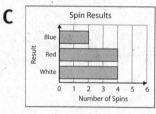

A

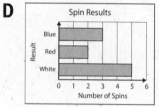

C

B

D

30 Micah tossed a number cube twenty times. The number 3 was tossed more than the number 4. Which line plot shows these results?

30 _____

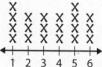

F

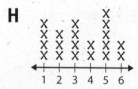

H

G

J

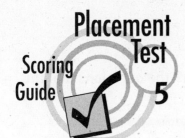

Placement Test 5

Scoring Guide

Student Name _____

For each part, mark the box under the number of correctly answered questions.

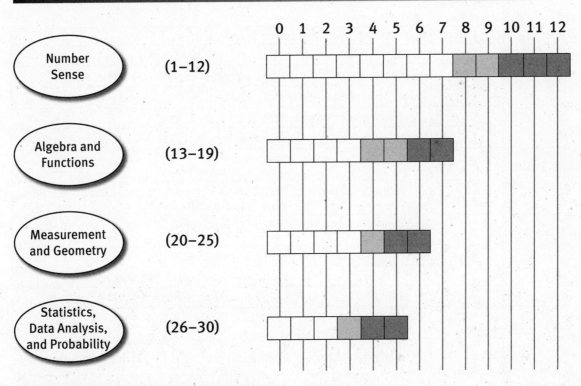

Mark the total number correct below.

Key: Consider this student for...

☐ *California Math Triumphs*

▨ Grade 5 Strategic Intervention—See page 52 for materials list.

▨ Grade 5

Placement Test 5

Student Name _____

In the column on the left, mark the questions that the student answered *incorrectly*.

Strand	May Need Intervention	Objective
Number Sense	☐ 1	read and write whole numbers in the millions
	☐ 2	compare whole numbers and decimals to two decimal places
	☐ 3	round whole numbers through the millions to the nearest thousand
	☐ 4	know the fraction and decimal equivalents for halves and fourths
	☐ 5	use concepts of negative numbers
	☐ 6	identify on a number line the relative position of decimals to 2 decimal places
	☐ 7	demonstrate an understanding of, and the ability to use, standard algorithms for the addition and subtraction of multidigit numbers
	☐ 8	demonstrate an understanding of, and the ability to use, standard algorithms for dividing a multidigit number by a one-digit number
	☐ 9	solve problem involving multiplication of multidigit numbers by two-digit numbers
	☐ 10	solve problem involving division of multidigit numbers by one-digit numbers
	☐ 11	understand that many whole numbers break down in different ways
	☐ 12	know that numbers such as 2, 3, 5, 7, and 11 are called prime numbers
Algebra and Functions	☐ 13	use letters, boxes, or other symbols to stand for any number in simple expressions or equations
	☐ 14 ☐ 15	interpret and evaluate mathematical expressions that use parentheses
	☐ 16	use and interpret formulas to answer questions about quantities and their relationships
	☐ 17	understand that an equation such as $y = 3x + 5$ is a prescription for determining a second number when a first number is given
	☐ 18	know and understand that equals added to equals are equal
	☐ 19	know and understand that equals multiplied by equals are equal
Measurement and Geometry	☐ 20	recognize that rectangles that have the same area can have different perimeters
	☐ 21	draw the points corresponding to linear relationships
	☐ 22	understand that the length of a horizontal line segment equals the difference of the x-coordinates
	☐ 23	understand that the length of a vertical line segment equals the difference of the y-coordinates
	☐ 24	identify lines that are parallel and perpendicular
	☐ 25	visualize, describe, and make models of geometric solids in terms of the number and shape of faces, edges, and vertices
Statistics, Data Analysis, and Probability	☐ 26 ☐ 27	identify the mode(s) for sets of categorical data and the mode(s), median, and any apparent outliers for numerical data sets
	☐ 28	systematically collect and represent data on a number line
	☐ 29	represent all possible outcomes for a simple probability situation in an organized way
	☐ 30	express outcomes of experimental probability situations verbally and numerically

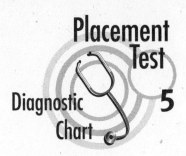

Placement Test
Diagnostic Chart
5

Student Performance Level	Number of Questions Correct	Suggestions for Intervention and Remediation
Intensive Intervention	0–15	Use *California Math Triumphs* to accelerate the achievement of students who are two or more years below grade level. Students should follow a personalized remediation plan. A variety of materials and instructional methods are recommended. For example, instruction and practice should be provided in print, technology, and hands-on lessons.
Strategic Intervention	16–21	Use the additional Intervention and Remediation materials listed on the next page. This list of materials can provide helpful resources for students who struggle in the traditional mathematics program. Strategic intervention allows students to continue to remain in the *California Mathematics: Concepts, Skills, and Problem Solving* program, while receiving the differentiated instruction they need. Teaching Tips and other resources are also listed in the Teacher Wraparound Edition.
Grade 5	22 or more	Use *California Mathematics: Concepts, Skills, and Problem Solving*. This student does not require overall intervention. However, based on the student's performance on the different sections, intervention may be required. For example, a student who missed 4 or more questions in the Measurement and Geometry section may require extra assistance as you cover these skills throughout the year.

A Special Note About Intervention

When using diagnostic tests, teachers should always question the reason behind the students' scores. Students can struggle with mathematics concepts for a variety of reasons. Personalized instruction is recommended for English language learners, students with specific learning disabilities, students with certain medical conditions, or for those who struggle with traditional instructional practice. Teachers should always consider the needs of the individual student when determining the best approach for instruction and program placement.

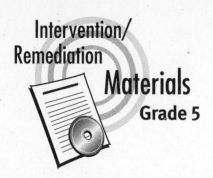

Intervention/Remediation Materials
Grade 5

Print Materials

Reteach Masters	A brief explanation, along with examples and exercises, for every lesson in the Student Edition. (Two pages for Problem-Solving Lessons and one page per lesson for all other lessons.) These masters are included in the Chapter Resource Masters.
Skills Practice Masters	Additional practice in computational and application exercises for each lesson in the Student Edition. These masters are included in the Chapter Resource Masters.
Homework Practice Masters	Additional practice in computational and spiral review exercises for each lesson in the Student Edition. These masters are included in the Chapter Resource Masters.
Study Guide and Intervention Workbook	A consumable version of the Study Guide and Intervention Masters for each lesson. Also available in Spanish.
Skills Practice Workbook	A consumable version of the Skills Practice Workbook Masters for each lesson. Also available in Spanish.
Practice Workbook	A consumable version of the Practice Masters for each lesson. Also available in Spanish.
Prerequisite Skills Workbook	Arithmetic study guide and practice pages for each of the prerequisite skills that review basic math concepts.

Technology Products

ExamView® Assessment Suite	Networkable software includes a Worksheet Builder to make worksheets and tests, a Student Module to take tests on-screen, and a Management System to keep student records.
Math Adventures with Dot and Ray	Provides entertaining activities and math games that use a problem-solving format.
Math Songs	Collections of songs, raps, and chants that are aligned to the California Standards.
Math Tool Chest	Contains inquiry-based concept building software with interactive representations of manipulatives.

Diagnostic and Placement Grade 5

This test contains 30 multiple-choice questions. Work each problem in the space on this page. Select the best answer. Write the letter of the answer on the blank at the right.

1 The number 3,040,012 is read as: 1 _____

    A three billion, forty million, twelve

    B three million, four thousand, twelve

    C three million, forty thousand, twelve

    D three hundred four thousand, twelve

2 Which number is the greatest?   2 _____

    F 13.1   **G** 5.22   **H** 2.92   **J** 1.08

3 What is 436,708 rounded to the nearest thousand?   3 _____

    A 436,000

    B 436,700

    C 436,800

    D 437,000

4 Which decimal is equivalent to $\frac{1}{2}$?   4 _____

    F 0.12   **G** 0.2   **H** 0.5   **J** 2.0

5 Which is the lowest temperature?   5 _____

    A 2°C   **B** 5°C   **C** −2°C   **D** −5°C

6 Which point could represent 2.34?   6 _____

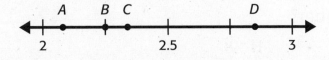

    F Point *A*   **G** Point *B*   **H** Point *C*   **J** Point *D*

7 47,821 − 3,045 =

    A 44,776

    B 44,786

    C 44,824

    D 44,876

7 _____

8 503 ÷ 4 =

    F 13 R1

    G 100 R3

    H 120 R3

    J 125 R3

8 _____

9 A school principal bought 46 pizzas for a party. Each pizza was cut into 12 slices. How many slices of pizza were there?

    A 138   **C** 552

    B 542   **D** 638

9 _____

10 Ms. Ayala has 54 pencils. She gives the same number of pencils to each of 7 students. She gives out as many pencils as she can. How many pencils does each student get?

    F 5   **H** 7

    G 6   **J** 8

10 _____

11 Which has the same value as $6 \times 4 \times 3$?

    A 24×3

    B 18×3

    C 10×3

    D 2×3

11 _____

12 Which is a prime number?

    F 7   **H** 9

    G 8   **J** 10

12 _____

13 Edmundo had 4 trading cards yesterday. He got some more trading cards today. Now he has 12 trading cards. If *n* represents the number of trading cards Edmundo got today, which equation is correct?

A $4 + 12 = n$

B $4 + n = 12$

C $n + 12 = 4$

D $n + 4 = 16$

13 _____

14 $40 - (10 + 2) =$

F 28 **G** 32 **H** 48 **J** 52

14 _____

15 $4 \times (9 - 3) =$

A 48

B 36

C 33

D 24

15 _____

16 Which equation below represents the area (*A*) of the rectangle in square centimeters?

16 _____

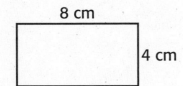

8 cm

4 cm

F $32 = A \times 8$

G $A = 8 \times 4$

H $A = (2 \times 4) + (2 \times 8)$

J $32 = (4 \times A)$

17 What is the value of *y* in the equation below if $x = 7$?

$$y = x + 3$$

A 21 **C** 7

B 10 **D** 4

17 _____

18 If $y = x + 6$, which statement is true?   18 _____

    F $y + 1 = x + 1$ **H** $y + 1 = x + 6$

    G $y + 1 = x + 5$ **J** $y + 1 = x + 7$

19 What number would make this number   19 _____
sentence true?

$$6 \times (8 - 3) = ? \times 5$$

    A 30   **B** 25   **C** 6   **D** 5

20 Lanu drew a rectangle 10 inches wide and   20 _____
20 inches long. Which rectangle described
below has the same area as Lanu's rectangle?

    F 5 inches wide and 25 inches long

    G 8 inches wide and 25 inches long

    H 15 inches wide and 15 inches long

    J 15 inches wide and 25 inches long

21 Kamila plotted the three points shown on   21 _____
the grid below. Kamila wants to draw a line
through the points and then plot another
point on the same line. Which point listed
below will be on the same line?

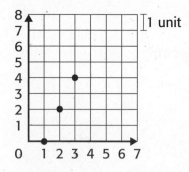

    A (4, 8)   **B** (5, 6)   **C** (5, 8)   **D** (6, 7)

22 What is the length of the line segment   22 _____
joining the points (3, 4) and (9, 4)?

    F 4 units   **G** 6 units   **H** 8 units   **J** 12 units

23 What is the length of the line segment joining the points (2, 5) and (2, 10)?

   A 2 units   **C** 5 units

   B 4 units   **D** 15 units

24 The polygon below has two right angles.

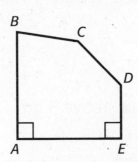

Which side of the polygon is parallel to side *AB*?

   F *BC*   **H** *DE*

   G *CD*   **J** *EA*

25 A rectangular prism is shown below.

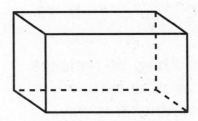

How many faces does a rectangular prism have?

   A 6   **B** 5   **C** 4   **D** 3

26 What is the median of this data?

      67, 98, 78, 75, 83, 44, 98

   F 44   **H** 78

   G 75   **J** 98

27 Find the mode of the following data.

      97, 88, 78, 77, 82, 57, 88

   A 97   **C** 82

   B 88   **D** 78

28 Marisol asked some classmates how many children were in their families. The results are listed below.

28 _____

1, 2, 1, 3, 3, 4, 1, 4, 4, 2

Marisol started this line plot to show the data.

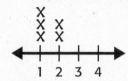

How many x's should Marisol draw above 3 on the line plot?

F 2   **G** 3   **H** 4   **J** 5

29 At a carnival game, you pick a door and then a curtain behind the door. There are 3 doors. There are 4 curtains behind each door. There is a different prize behind each curtain. How many different prizes are there?

29 _____

A 3   **B** 4   **C** 7   **D** 12

30 Booker chooses a marble from a bag. He replaces the marble and then chooses another marble from the bag. He chooses 40 marbles this way, and 8 of them are red. Based on Booker's experiment, which is the probability of choosing a red marble?

30 _____

F 1 out of 5

G 1 out of 8

H 8 out of 32

J 32 out of 40

Placement Test 6
Scoring Guide

Student Name _____

For each part, mark the box under the number of correctly answered questions.

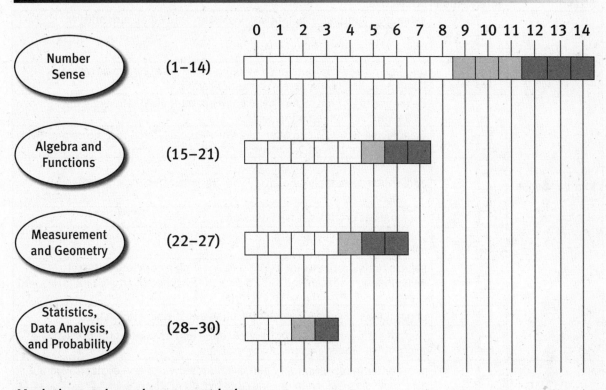

Mark the total number correct below.

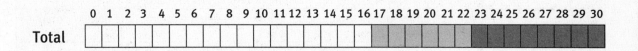

Total

Key: Consider this student for...

☐ *California Math Triumphs*

◩ Grade 6 Strategic Intervention—See page 62 for materials list.

◼ Grade 6

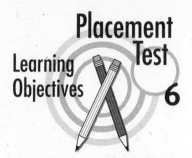

Placement Test 6

Learning Objectives

Student Name _____

In the column on the left, mark the questions that the student answered *incorrectly*.

Strand	May Need Intervention	Objective
Number Sense	☐ 1	estimate, round, and manipulate very large and small numbers
	☐ 2 ☐ 3	interpret, find, and compute percents
	☐ 4	understand and compute positive integer powers of nonnegative integers; compute examples as repeated multiplication
	☐ 5	determine the prime factors of all numbers through 50 and write the numbers as the product of their prime factors
	☐ 6	identify and represent on a number line decimals, fractions, mixed numbers, and positive and negative integers
	☐ 7 ☐ 8 ☐ 9	add, subtract, multiply, and divide with decimals and negative integers
	☐ 10	demonstrate proficiency with division
	☐ 11	solve simple problems involving the addition and subtraction of fractions and mixed numbers
	☐ 12	solve simple problems including ones arising in concrete situations, involving the addition and subtraction of fractions and mixed numbers and express answers in the simplest form
	☐ 13	understand the concept of multiplication and division of fractions
	☐ 14	compute and perform simple multplication and division of fractions and apply these procedures to solving problems
Algebra and Functions	☐ 15 ☐ 16	use a letter to represent an unknown number; write and evalutate simple algebraic expressions in one variable by substitution
	☐ 17	use information taken from a graph or equation to answer questions about a problem situation
	☐ 18	know and use the distributive property in equations and expressions with variables.
	☐ 19	identify and graph ordered pairs in the four quadrants of the coordinate plane
	☐ 20 ☐ 21	solve problems involving linear functions with integer values; write equations; and graph the resulting ordered pairs of intergers
Measurement and Geometry	☐ 22	understand the concept of volume and use the appropriate units to compute the volume of rectangular solids
	☐ 23 ☐ 24	measure, identify, and draw angles, perpendicular and parallel lines, rectangles, and triangles by using appropriate tools
	☐ 25	derive and use formula for the area of a triangle and of a parallelogram
	☐ 26	construct a cube and rectangular box from two-dimensional patterns and use these patterns to compute the surface area for these objects
	☐ 27	know that the sum of the angles of any triangleis 180° and the sum of the angles of any quadrilateral is 360° and use this information to solve problems
Statistics, Data Analysis, and Probability	☐ 28	know the concepts of mean, median, and mode; compute and compare simple examples to show that they may differ
	☐ 29	identify ordered pairs of data from a graph and interpret the meaning of the data in terms of the situation depicted by the graph
	☐ 30	know how to write ordered pairs correctly; for example, (x, y)

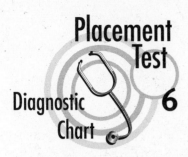

Placement Test 6
Diagnostic Chart

Student Performance Level	Number of Questions Correct	Suggestions for Intervention and Remediation
Intensive Intervention	0–16	Use *California Math Triumphs* to accelerate the achievement of students who are two or more years below grade level. Students should follow a personalized remediation plan. A variety of materials and instructional methods are recommended. For example, instruction and practice should be provided in print, technology, and hands-on lessons.
Strategic Intervention	17–22	Use the additional Intervention and Remediation materials listed on the next page. This list of materials can provide helpful resources for students who struggle in the traditional mathematics program. Strategic intervention allows students to continue to remain in the *California Mathematics: Concepts, Skills, and Problem Solving* program, while receiving the differentiated instruction they need. Teaching Tips and other resources are also listed in the Teacher Wraparound Edition.
Grade 6	**23 or more**	Use *California Mathematics: Concepts, Skills, and Problem Solving*. This student does not require overall intervention. However, based on the student's performance on the different sections, intervention may be required. For example, a student who missed 4 or more questions in the Measurement and Geometry section may require extra assistance as you cover these skills throughout the year.

A Special Note About Intervention

When using diagnostic tests, teachers should always question the reason behind the students' scores. Students can struggle with mathematics concepts for a variety of reasons. Personalized instruction is recommended for English language learners, students with specific learning disabilities, students with certain medical conditions, or for those who struggle with traditional instructional practice. Teachers should always consider the needs of the individual student when determining the best approach for instruction and program placement.

Intervention/Remediation Materials
Grade 6

Print Materials

Reteach Masters	A brief explanation, along with examples and exercises, for every lesson in the Student Edition. (Two pages for Problem-Solving Lessons and one page per lesson for all other lessons.) These masters are included in the Chapter Resource Masters.
Skills Practice Masters	Additional practice in computational and application exercises for each lesson in the Student Edition. These masters are included in the Chapter Resource Masters.
Homework Practice Masters	Additional practice in computational and spiral review exercises for each lesson in the Student Edition. These masters are included in the Chapter Resource Masters.
Study Guide and Intervention Workbook	A consumable version of the Study Guide and Intervention Masters for each lesson. Also available in Spanish.
Skills Practice Workbook	A consumable version of the Skills Practice Workbook Masters for each lesson. Also available in Spanish.
Practice Workbook	A consumable version of the Practice Masters for each lesson. Also available in Spanish.
Prerequisite Skills Workbook	Arithmetic study guide and practice pages for each of the prerequisite skills that review basic math concepts.

Technology Products

ExamView® Assessment Suite	Networkable software includes a Worksheet Builder to make worksheets and tests, a Student Module to take tests on-screen, and a Management System to keep student records.
MindJogger Videoquizzes	Chapter review provided in a game-show format.
Vocabulary PuzzleMaker Software	Improves students' mathematics vocabulary using crossword puzzles, scrambles, and word searches.
Problem-Solving Practice Masters	Additional practice in application exercises for each lesson in the Student Edition.

Diagnostic and Placement Grade 6

Name _____

Date _____

This test contains 30 multiple-choice questions. Work each problem in the space on this page. Select the best answer. Write the letter of the answer on the blank at the right.

1 What is 4,738,526 rounded to the nearest hundred thousand?   **1** _____

    A 5,000,000   **C** 4,739,000

    B 4,740,000   **D** 4,700,000

2 What is 30% of 330?   **2** _____

    F 99   **H** 300

    G 110   **J** 990

3 The school band sold 200 tickets to their concert. If 90 of the tickets were adult tickets, what percent of the tickets sold were adult tickets?   **3** _____

    A 18%   **C** 55%

    B 45%   **D** 90%

4 $6^4 =$ **4** _____

    F $6 + 6 + 6 + 6$ **H** $4 + 4 + 4 + 4 + 4 + 4$

    G $6 \times 6 \times 6 \times 6$ **J** $4 \times 4 \times 4 \times 4 \times 4 \times 4$

5 What is the prime factorization of 18?   **5** _____

    A 3×6 **C** 2×3^3

    B 2×9 **D** 2×3^2

6 Which point on the number line is located at -3?   **6** _____

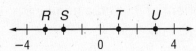

    F R   **G** S   **H** T   **J** U

California Diagnostic and Placement Tests

7 $3.45 \times 2.6 =$

    A 8.64   **B** 8.97   **C** 86.4   **D** 89.7

7 _____

8 Mateo ordered 4 ham sandwiches at the deli. The total amount was $30.52. How much did each sandwich cost?

    F $7.63   **G** $7.83   **H** $12.63   **J** $122.08

8 _____

9 Chrissy is knitting a scarf. The scarf is 4.6 feet long. If she knits another 1.75 feet, how long will the scarf be?

    A 6.35 feet   **B** 5.81 feet   **C** 5.35 feet   **D** 2.85 feet

9 _____

10 $29,412 \div 43 =$

    F 684   **G** 698   **H** 703   **J** 730

10 _____

11 $4\frac{1}{4} + 1\frac{1}{3} =$

    A $5\frac{1}{7}$ **B** $5\frac{1}{6}$ **C** $5\frac{2}{7}$ **D** $5\frac{7}{12}$

11 _____

12 Nate had $6\frac{3}{5}$ yards of fabric. He used $3\frac{1}{2}$ yards of fabric to make a pillow. How much fabric does he have left?

    F $3\frac{1}{10}$ yards   **G** $3\frac{1}{5}$ yards   **H** $3\frac{2}{3}$ yards   **J** $4\frac{1}{10}$ yards

12 _____

13 $\frac{3}{4} \times \frac{2}{5} =$

    A $\frac{3}{10}$ **B** $\frac{7}{20}$ **C** $\frac{5}{9}$ **D** $1\frac{7}{8}$

13 _____

14 Isabel has $2\frac{1}{8}$ cups of sugar. Each batch of cookies uses $\frac{3}{4}$ cup of sugar. How many batches of cookies can Isabel bake?

    F $1\frac{3}{8}$ **G** $1\frac{19}{32}$ **H** $2\frac{5}{6}$ **J** $2\frac{7}{8}$

14 _____

15 Which expression represents the quotient of 31 and a number?

    A $31 \times n$ **C** $31 - n$

    B $31 + n$ **D** $31 \div n$

15 _____

16 If $y = 4$, what is the value of $y \times 7 + 3$?

    F 24   **G** 25   **H** 31   **J** 40

16 _____

17 $m - 1\frac{1}{3}$

Which situation could be described by the expression above?

A A roll of ribbon is m yards long. Miranda cut $1\frac{1}{3}$ yards of ribbon from the roll.

B A roll of ribbon is $1\frac{1}{3}$ yards long. Miranda cut m yards of ribbon from the roll.

C A roll of ribbon is m yards long. Miranda used $1\frac{1}{3}$ rolls of ribbon.

D A roll of ribbon is m yards long. Miranda cut the ribbon into pieces $1\frac{1}{3}$ yard in length.

18 What value for t makes this equation true?

$$6 \times 52 = (6 \times t) + (6 \times 2)$$

F 5   **G** 6   **H** 50   **J** 52

19 The map below shows where four of Danny's friends live.

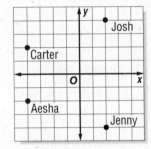

Which friend lives at the point $(-4, 2)$?

A Carter   **B** Jenny   **C** Josh   **D** Aesha

20 Which equation shows the relationship between the x and y values in this table?

x	y
-4	-2
-1	1
2	4
4	6
10	12

F $y = x - 2$ **H** $y = x + 2$

G $x = y + 2$ **J** $y = \frac{x}{2}$

21 Line b is represented by the equation $x = 3$.

21 _____

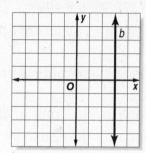

Which ordered pair is located on line b?

A (2, 3) **B** (3, −2) **C** (0, 3) **D** (0, 0)

22 A rectangular sandbox has a length of 60 inches, a width of 40 inches and a depth of 6 inches. What volume of sand can the sandbox hold?

22 _____

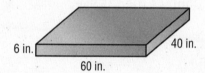

6 in. 40 in.
60 in.

F 240 cubic inches **H** 2,400 cubic inches
G 360 cubic inches **J** 14,400 cubic inches

23 Which is closest to the measure of the angle shown below?

23 _____

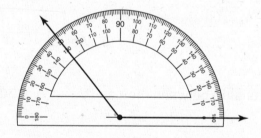

A 50° **B** 80° **C** 130° **D** 180°

24 Which of the following pairs of lines appear to be parallel?

24 _____

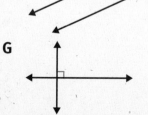

F

G

H

J

25 In the figure below, *ABCD* is a parallelogram.

25 _____

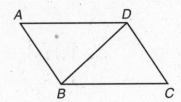

If the area of triangle *ABD* is 48 square centimeters, what is the area of *ABCD*?

    A 24 square centimeters   **C** 96 square centimeters

    B 48 square centimeters   **D** 192 square centimeters

26 Mr. Trevino folded this pattern to make a box.

26 _____

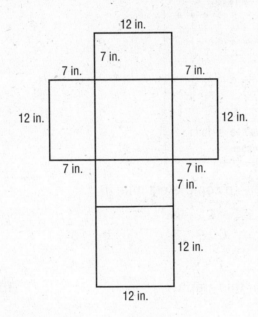

What is the surface area of the box?

    F 128 square inches   **H** 480 square inches

    G 336 square inches   **J**   624 square inches

27 What is the measure of angle *r* in the figure below?

27 _____

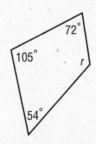

    A 49°   **B** 129°   **C** 169°   **D** 231°

28 The basketball team's scores for 5 games are listed below.

35, 48, 24, 31, 47

What is the mean of the scores?

F 24 **G** 35 **H** 37 **J** 185

29 Gabe is training for a race. After every run, his coach records how many minutes it took Gabe to run a mile. The graph below shows Gabe's times.

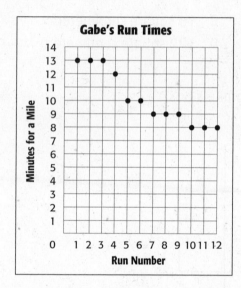

How many runs did it take for Gabe to complete a mile in less than 10 minutes?

A 5 **B** 7 **C** 9 **D** 10

30 Which point represents $(3, -4)$ on this graph?

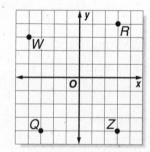

F point Q **G** point R **H** point W **J** point Z

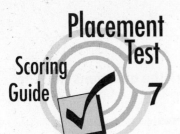

Placement Test 7
Scoring Guide

Student Name _____

For each part, mark the box under the number of correctly answered questions.

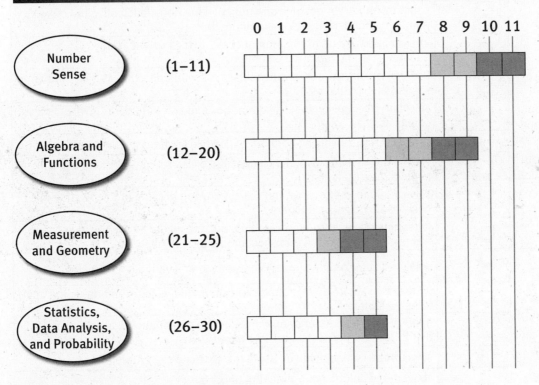

Mark the total number correct below.

Total 0 1 2 3 4 5 6 7 8 9 10 11 12 13 14 15 16 17 18 19 20 21 22 23 24 25 26 27 28 29 30

Key: Consider this student for...

- ☐ *California Math Triumphs*
- ☐ Grade 7 Strategic Intervention—See page 72 for materials list.
- ☐ Grade 7

Placement Test 7

Learning Objectives

In the column on the left, mark the questions that the student answered *incorrectly*.

Strand	May Need Intervention	Objective
Number Sense	☐ 1 ☐ 2	compare and order positive and negative fractions, decimals, and mixed numbers and place them on a number line
	☐ 3	interpret and use ratios in different contexts to show the relative sizes of two quantities, using appropriate notations
	☐ 4 ☐ 5	use proportions to solve problem; use cross-multiplication as a method of solving such problems
	☐ 6	calculate given percentages of quantities and solve problems involving discounts at sales, interest earned and tips
	☐ 7	solve problems involving addition of positive fractions
	☐ 8	explain the meaning of multiplicatioin and division of positive fractions and perform the calculations
	☐ 9 ☐ 10	solve addition, subtraction, multiplication, and division problems, that use positive and negative integers
	☐ 11	determine the least common multiple and the greatest common divisor of whole numbers; use them to solve problems with fractions
Algebra and Functions	☐ 12 ☐ 13	write and solve on-step linear equations in one variable
	☐ 14	write and evaluate an algebraic expression for a given situation, using up to three variables
	☐ 15	apply algebraic order of operations and the commutative, associative, and distributive properties to evaluate expressions
	☐ 16	solve problems manually by using the correct order of operations
	☐ 17	convert one unit of meaurement to another
	☐ 18	demonstrate an understanding that rate is a measure of one quantity per unit value of another quantity
	☐ 19	solve problems involving rates, average speed, distance, and time
	☐ 20	use variables in expressions describing geometric quantities
Measurement and Geometry	☐ 21	understand the concept of a constant such as π; know the formulas for the circumference and area of a circle
	☐ 22	know common estimates of π and use these values to estimate and calculate the circumference and the area of circles
	☐ 23	identify angles as vertical, adjacent, complementary, or supplementary and provide descriptions of these terms
	☐ 24	use properties of complementary and supplementary angles and the sum of the angles of a triangle to solve problems involving an unknown angle
	☐ 25	draw quadrilaterals and triangles form given information
Statistics, Data Analysis, and Probability	☐ 26	understand how additional data added to data sets may affect the computations
	☐ 27	identify claims based on statistical data and, in simple cases, evaluate the validity of the claims
	☐ 28	represent all the possible outcomes for compound events in a organized way and express the theoretical probability of each outcome
	☐ 29	represent probabilities as ratios, proportions, decimals between 0 and 1, and percentages between 0 and 100; know that if P is the probability of an event, $1 - P$ is the probability of an event not occurring
	☐ 30	understand the difference between independent and dependent events

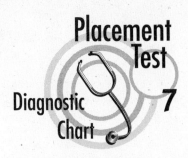

Placement Test
Diagnostic Chart 7

Student Performance Level	Number of Questions Correct	Suggestions for Intervention and Remediation
Intensive Intervention	0–17	Use *California Math Triumphs* to accelerate the achievement of students who are two or more years below grade level. Students should follow a personalized remediation plan. A variety of materials and instructional methods are recommended. For example, instruction and practice should be provided in print, technology, and hands-on lessons.
Strategic Intervention	18–23	Use the additional Intervention and Remediation materials listed on the next page. This list of materials can provide helpful resources for students who struggle in the traditional mathematics program. Strategic intervention allows students to continue to remain in the *California Mathematics: Concepts, Skills, and Problem Solving* program, while receiving the differentiated instruction they need. Teaching Tips and other resources are also listed in the Teacher Wraparound Edition.
Grade 7	24 or more	Use *California Mathematics: Concepts, Skills, and Problem Solving*. This student does not require overall intervention. However, based on the student's performance on the different sections, intervention may be required. For example, a student who missed 3 or more questions in the Measurement and Geometry section may require extra assistance as you cover these skills throughout the year.

A Special Note About Intervention

When using diagnostic tests, teachers should always question the reason behind the students' scores. Students can struggle with mathematics concepts for a variety of reasons. Personalized instruction is recommended for English language learners, students with specific learning disabilities, students with certain medical conditions, or for those who struggle with traditional instructional practice. Teachers should always consider the needs of the individual student when determining the best approach for instruction and program placement.

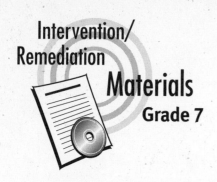

Intervention/Remediation Materials
Grade 7

Print Materials

Reteach Masters	A brief explanation, along with examples and exercises, for every lesson in the Student Edition. (Two pages for Problem-Solving Lessons and one page per lesson for all other lessons.) These masters are included in the Chapter Resource Masters.
Skills Practice Masters	Additional practice in computational and application exercises for each lesson in the Student Edition. These masters are included in the Chapter Resource Masters.
Homework Practice Masters	Additional practice in computational and spiral review exercises for each lesson in the Student Edition. These masters are included in the Chapter Resource Masters.
Study Guide and Intervention Workbook	A consumable version of the Study Guide and Intervention Masters for each lesson. Also available in Spanish.
Skills Practice Workbook	A consumable version of the Skills Practice Workbook Masters for each lesson. Also available in Spanish.
Practice Workbook	A consumable version of the Practice Masters for each lesson. Also available in Spanish.
Prerequisite Skills Workbook	Arithmetic study guide and practice pages for each of the prerequisite skills that review basic math concepts.

Technology Products

ExamView® Assessment Suite	Networkable software includes a Worksheet Builder to make worksheets and tests, a Student Module to take tests on-screen, and a Management System to keep student records.
MindJogger Videoquizzes	Chapter review provided in a game-show format.
Vocabulary PuzzleMaker Software	Improves students' mathematics vocabulary using crossword puzzles, scrambles, and word searches.
Problem-Solving Practice Masters	Additional practice in application exercises for each lesson in the Student Edition.

Diagnostic and Placement
Grade 7

Name _____

Date _____

This test contains 30 multiple-choice questions. Work each problem in the space on this page. Select the best answer. Write the letter of the answer on the blank at the right.

1 Which set of numbers is in order from least to greatest?

1 _____

    A $-3.1, -\frac{3}{8}, \frac{5}{8}, \frac{4}{5}$

    B $-\frac{3}{8}, -3.1, \frac{5}{8}, \frac{4}{5}$

    C $\frac{4}{5}, \frac{5}{8}, -\frac{3}{8}, -3.1$

    D $-3.1, -\frac{3}{8}, \frac{4}{5}, \frac{5}{8}$

2 Which number could be the value of point A?

2 _____

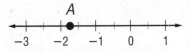

    F $-2\frac{1}{4}$ **H** $-1\frac{3}{4}$

    G -2 **J** $-1\frac{1}{4}$

3 For every 12 slices of pizza sold at Ping's Pizza Shop, 3 are pepperoni, 4 are sausage, and the rest are cheese. What is the ratio of pepperoni to cheese?

3 _____

    A   3:12   **C**   3:4

    B   3:5   **D**   5:3

4 Horatio jogs 5 laps around a track in 8 minutes. At the same rate, how long would it take him to jog 12 laps?

4 _____

    F   15 minutes   **H**   19.2 minutes

    G   15.6 minutes   **J**   20 minutes

5 Marita earned $50 for baby-sitting 8 hours. At the same rate how much would she earn for baby-sitting 10 hours?

5 _____

    A $60.00   **C** $62.00

    B $60.25   **D** $62.50

        California Diagnostic and Placement Tests

6 Aleta went to dinner. The bill was $36. She gave the waiter a 15% tip. What was the total amount Aleta spent on the food and the tip?

    F $36.15   **H** $38.40

    G $37.50   **J** $41.40

7 Sara walked $1\frac{3}{10}$ miles to her friend's house. Then she walked $\frac{3}{4}$ mile to the library. How far did Sara walk in all?

    A $1\frac{3}{7}$ miles   **C** $2\frac{1}{20}$ miles

    B $1\frac{9}{10}$ miles   **D** $2\frac{1}{10}$ miles

8 Which multiplication is shown by the picture below?

    F $\frac{1}{5} \times \frac{1}{4}$ **H** $\frac{2}{20} \times \frac{3}{20}$

    G $\frac{2}{5} \times \frac{3}{5}$ **J** $\frac{2}{5} \times \frac{3}{4}$

9 Alvin was testing an elevator in a new office building. He started on the 1st floor. He rode the elevator up 5 floors, then down 3 floors, then up 7 floors, and then down 1 floor. On what floor did he stop?

    A 8th floor   **C** 15th floor

    B 9th floor   **D** 17th floor

10 Simplify $-8 + 17(-3)$.

    F -59 **H** -27

    G -28 **J** 6

11 Kono divided the numerator and denominator of $\frac{48}{72}$ by the same number to simplify the fraction in one step. By what number did he divide?

    A 2   **C** 16

    B 12   **D** 24

12 If $12x = 99$, what is the value of x?

12 _____

    F $0.\overline{12}$ **H** 87

    G 8.25   **J** 1188

13 What is the solution to the equation $-8 + p = -2$?

13 _____

    A $p = -10$ **C** $p = 6$

    B $p = -6$ **D** $p = 10$

14 Erin has 87 baseball cards in her collection. Erin's number of cards is x less than Oscar's number of cards. Which expression represents Oscar's number of cards?

14 _____

    F $87 + x$ **H** $x - 87$

    G $87 - x$ **J** $87x$

15 What is the value of the expression below?

15 _____

$$16 - 3(8 + 2)^2$$

    A -884 **C** -188

    B -284 **D** 1300

16 Simplify the expression $7^2 - 4^2 \times 3$.

16 _____

    F -10 **H** 18

    G 1   **J** 99

17 A package weighs $2\frac{3}{4}$ pounds. What is the weight of the package in ounces?

17 _____

    A 35 ounces   **C** 43.7 ounces

    B 36.8 ounces   **D** 44 ounces

18 Which of the following boxes of cereal costs the least per ounce?

18 _____

    F 10 ounces for $3.19   **H** 15 ounces for $4.59

    G 12 ounces for $3.49   **J** 20 ounces for $5.99

19 A landscaper covers 8,400 square feet with fertilizer in 45 minutes. At the same rate, how many square feet would she cover in 1 hour?

19 _____

    A 10,500 square feet   **C** 12,600 square feet

    B 11,200 square feet   **D** 18,667 square feet

20 A triangle has a height that is 3 units longer than its base. If *b* represents the base and *h* represents the height, which equation represents the area of the triangle?

F $A = \frac{1}{2}(b + 3)$

H $A = \frac{1}{2}b(b + 3)$

G $A = \frac{1}{2}(h + 3)$

J $A = \frac{1}{2}(h + 3)$

21 A circle has a radius of 8 centimeters. What is the circumference of the circle?

21 _____

A 8π centimeters

C 64π centimeters

B 16π centimeters

D 128π centimeters

22 The can shown below is a cylinder.

22 _____

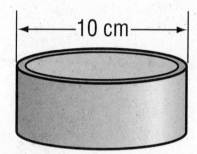

Which is the best estimation for the area of the top of the can?

F 25 cm^2

H 75 cm^2

G 30 cm^2

J 100 cm^2

23 In the diagram below, which is a pair of vertical angles?

23 _____

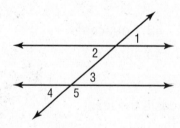

A $\angle 1$ and $\angle 2$

C $\angle 1$ and $\angle 4$

B $\angle 1$ and $\angle 3$

D $\angle 1$ and $\angle 5$

24 What is the value of x in the diagram below?

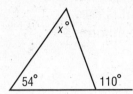

F 36 **G** 54 **H** 56 **J** 70

25 Which picture below is an obtuse isosceles triangle?

A

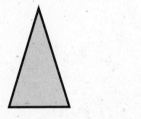

C

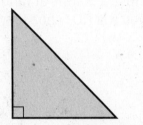

B

D

26 Kim's quiz grades in math are 80, 80, 88, and 92. Which of the following measures will NOT change if Kim receives a 50 on her next quiz?

F median **H** mode
G mean **J** range

27 A company has five employees. Their annual earnings, in dollars, are shown below.

24,000	24,000	28,000	30,000	125,000

Which of the following measures best represents the typical annual earnings of an employee of the company?

A mean **C** mode
B median **D** range

28 Four cards numbered 1, 5, 8, and 9 are placed in a
bag. A card is drawn at random and then replaced.
Then a card is drawn at random again. What is the
probability that both cards drawn have the number 9?

F $\frac{1}{16}$ H $\frac{1}{4}$

G $\frac{1}{9}$ J $\frac{1}{2}$

29 There are 10 marbles in a bag—1 blue, 4 yellow, 3 red,
and 2 white. If you chose a marble at random, which is
the probability that you will NOT choose white?

A 20%

B 25%

C 75%

D 80%

30 There are 8 cans of soft drink in a cooler. There are
3 cola, 3 orange, and 2 grape. Carlos chooses a can of
soft drink at random and drinks it. Then Lucy chooses
a can of soft drink at random from the remaining drinks.
What is the probability that both Carlos and Lucy get grape?

F $\frac{1}{32}$

G $\frac{1}{28}$

H $\frac{1}{16}$

J $\frac{1}{14}$

Placement Test
Scoring Guide
Algebra 1

Student Name _____

For each part, mark the box under the number of correctly answered questions.

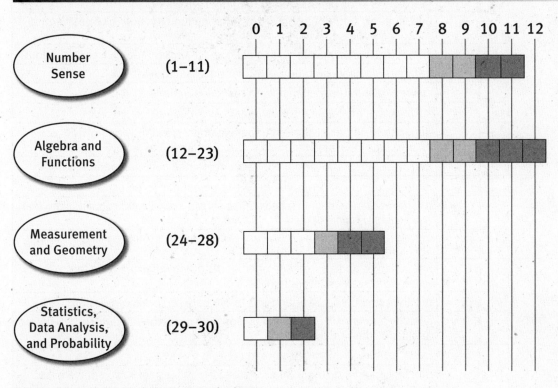

		0 1 2 3 4 5 6 7 8 9 10 11 12
Number Sense	(1–11)	
Algebra and Functions	(12–23)	
Measurement and Geometry	(24–28)	
Statistics, Data Analysis, and Probability	(29–30)	

Mark the total number correct below.

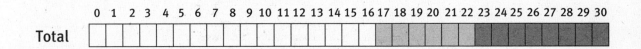

Total   0 1 2 3 4 5 6 7 8 9 10 11 12 13 14 15 16 17 18 19 20 21 22 23 24 25 26 27 28 29 30

Key: Consider this student for...

☐ *California Algebra Readiness*

▨ Algebra 1 Remediation Ancillary—See page 82 for materials list.

▦ Algebra 1

Placement Test
Learning Objectives
Algebra 1

Student Name _____

In the column on the left, mark the questions that the student answered *incorrectly*.

Strand	May Need Intervention		Objective
Number Sense	☐	1	read, write, and compare rational numbers in general
	☐	2	add, subtract, multiply, and divide rational numbers and take positive rational numbers to whole-number power
	☐	3	convert fractions to percents and use these representations in computations
	☐	4	differentiate between rational and irrational numbers
	☐	5	convert terminating decimals into reduced fractions
	☐	6	solve problems that involve discounts and markups
	☐	7	understand negative whole-number exponents; multiply and divide expressions involving exponents with a common base
	☐	8	add and subtract fractions; use factoring to find common denominators
	☐	9	multiply, divide, and simplify rational numbers by using exponent rules
	☐	10	use the inverse relationship between raising to a power and extracting the root of a perfect square integer
	☐	11	understand the meaning of the absolute value of a number; determine the absolute value of real numbers
Algebra and Functions	☐	12	use variables and appropriate operations to write an expression that represents a verbal description
	☐	13	use the correct order of operations to evaluate algebraic expressions
	☐	14	simplify numerical expressions by applying properties of rational numbers and justify the process used
	☐	15	
	☐	16	use algebraic terminology correctly
	☐	17	multiply and divide monomials; extend the process of taking powers and extracting roots to monomials when the latter results in a monomial with an integer exponent
	☐	18	solve problems and graph functions of the form $y = nx^2$ and $y = nx^3$
	☐	19	graph linear functions
	☐	20	
	☐	21	plot the values of quantities whose ratios are always the same, fit a line to the plot and understand that the slope of the line equals the ratio of the quantities
	☐	22	solve two-step linear equations and inequalities in one variable over the rational numbers
	☐	23	solve multi-step problems involving average speed
Measurement and Geometry	☐	24	use measures expressed as rates and measures expressed as products to solve problems; check the units of the solutions
	☐	25	use formulas for finding the area of basic two-dimensional figures
	☐	26	know and understand the Pythagorean theorem and its converse and use it to find the length of the missing side of a right triangle
	☐	27	demonstrate an understanding of what congruence means about the relationships between the sides and angles of the two figures
	☐	28	identify elements of three-dimensional geometric objects and describe how two or more objects are related in space
Statistics, Data Analysis, and Probability	☐	29	know various forms of display for data sets, including a stem-and-leaf plot or box-and-whisker plot; use the forms to display a single set of data
	☐	30	understand the meaning of, and compute median of a set of data

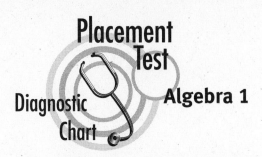

Placement Test
Diagnostic Chart
Algebra 1

Student Performance Level	Number of Questions Correct	Suggestions for Intervention and Remediation
Intensive Intervention	**0–16**	Use *California Algebra Readiness* to accelerate the achievement of students who are below grade level. Students should follow a personalized remediation plan. A variety of materials and instructional methods are recommended. For example, instruction and practice should be provided in print, technology, and hands-on lessons.
Strategic Intervention	**17–22**	Use the additional Intervention and Remediation materials listed on the next page. This list of materials can provide helpful resources for students who struggle in the traditional mathematics program. Strategic intervention allows students to continue to remain in the *California Mathematics: Concepts, Skills, and Problem Solving* program, while receiving the differentiated instruction they need. Teaching Tips and other resources are also listed in the Teacher Wraparound Edition.
Algebra 1	**23 or more**	Use *California Algebra 1: Concepts, Skills, and Problem Solving*. This student does not require overall intervention. However, based on the student's performance on the different sections, intervention may be required. For example, a student who missed 3 or more questions in the Measurement and Geometry section may require extra assistance as you cover these skills throughout the year.

A Special Note About Intervention

When using diagnostic tests, teachers should always question the reason behind the students' scores. Students can struggle with mathematics concepts for a variety of reasons. Personalized instruction is recommended for English language learners, students with specific learning disabilities, students with certain medical conditions, or for those who struggle with traditional instructional practice. Teachers should always consider the needs of the individual student when determining the best approach for instruction and program placement.

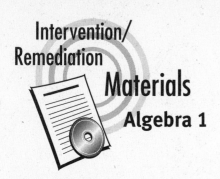

Intervention/ Remediation Materials
Algebra 1

Print Materials	
Quick Review Math Handbook	A comprehensive reference of important mathematical terms and concepts to help build math literacy. Also available in Spanish.
Study Guide and Intervention Masters	A brief explanation, along with examples and exercises, for every lesson in the Student Edition. These masters are included in the Chapter Resource Masters.
Skills Practice Masters	Additional practice in computational and application exercises for each lesson in the Student Edition. These masters are included in the Chapter Resource Masters.
Practice Masters	Additional practice in computational and spiral review exercises for each lesson in the Student Edition. These masters are included in the Chapter Resource Masters.
Study Guide and Intervention Workbook	A consumable version of the Study Guide and Intervention Masters for each lesson. Also available in Spanish.
Skills Practice Workbook	A consumable version of the Skills Practice Workbook Masters for each lesson. Also available in Spanish.
Practice Workbook	A consumable version of the Practice Masters for each lesson. Also available in Spanish.
Prerequisite Skills Workbook: Remediation and Intervention	Arithmetic study guide and practice pages for each of the prerequisite skills that review basic math concepts. Also available in Spanish.

Technology Products	
ExamView Pro® Assessment Suite	Networkable software includes a Worksheet Builder to make worksheets and tests, a Student Module to take tests on-screen, and a Management System to keep student records.
Mathematics Super DVDs	Includes: MindJogger Plus, a chapter review provided in a game-show format, and What's Math Got to Do With It? Real Life Math Videos that show students how math is used in everyday situations through engaging videos.
Problem-Solving Practice Masters	Additional practice in application exercises for each lesson in the Student Edition.

Name _____

Date _____

This test contains 30 multiple-choice questions. Work each problem in the space on this page. Select the best answer. Write the letter of the answer on the blank at the right.

1 Which set of numbers is in order from least to greatest?   1 _____

    A 2.07×10^4, 2.07×10^{-3}, -2.07×10^{-2}, -2.07×10^2

    B 2.07×10^{-3}, -2.07×10^{-2}, -2.07×10^2, 2.07×10^4

    C -2.07×10^2, -2.07×10^{-2}, 2.07×10^{-3}, 2.07×10^4

    D -2.07×10^{-2}, -2.07×10^2, 2.07×10^{-3}, 2.07×10^4

2 $\dfrac{3\frac{3}{5}}{\frac{2}{5}} - (0.4)^2 =$ 2 _____

    F -0.16 **H**   7.4

    G   1.28   **J**   8.84

3 Luis saved $\frac{5}{8}$ of his pay. What percent of his pay did he save?   3 _____

    A   6.25%   **C**   62.5%

    B   40%   **D**   72.5%

4 Which is an irrational number?   4 _____

    F $\sqrt{2}$ **H** $5\frac{4}{9}$

    G $\sqrt{9}$ **J** 3^2

5 $0.04 =$ 5 _____

    A $\frac{1}{40}$ **C** $\frac{1}{4}$

    B $\frac{1}{25}$ **D** $\frac{2}{5}$

6 A bookstore manager paid $12 for a book and used a 60%   6 _____
markup to set the regular price of the book. Jamie bought
the book from the store for 10% off of the regular price.
How much did Jamie pay for the book?

    F $17.28   **H** $19.20

    G $18.00   **J** $20.40

7 $\dfrac{\left(\frac{4}{5}\right)^{-3} \times \left(\frac{4}{5}\right)^{8}}{\left(\frac{4}{5}\right)^{2}} =$

    A $\left(\frac{4}{5}\right)^{-48}$ **C** $\left(\frac{4}{5}\right)^{3}$

    B $\left(\frac{4}{5}\right)^{-12}$ **D** $\left(\frac{4}{5}\right)^{7}$

7 _____

8 $\dfrac{8}{65} + \dfrac{1}{25} =$

    F $\dfrac{9}{325}$ **H** $\dfrac{53}{325}$

    G $\dfrac{1}{10}$ **J** $\dfrac{49}{65}$

8 _____

9 $\dfrac{2^{2} \cdot 8^{2}}{2^{-1} \cdot 5^{-2} \cdot 8^{3}} =$

    A 0.04   **C** 18.75

    B 10   **D** 25

9 _____

10 A square garden has an area of 144 square feet. What is the length of one side of the garden?

    F 3 feet   **H** 36 feet

    G 12 feet   **J** 72 feet

10 _____

11 $-|12 - 5| + |3 - 8| =$

    A -12 **C** 2

    B -2 **D** 12

11 _____

12 Which algebraic expression represents the phrase "6 less than the sum of x and the square of x"?

    F $x + x^{2} - 6$ **H** $6 - x + x^{2}$

    G $x + \sqrt{x} - 6$ **J** $6 - (x + x^{2})$

12 _____

13 Given $a = 3$ and $b = -5$, evaluate $4a - 2(b + 3)$.

    A -20 **C** 8

    B -8 **D** 16

13 _____

14 Which expression is equivalent to
−3(8 − 10)?

    F −24 − 30   **H** −24 + 30

    G −24 − 10   **J** 24 − 30

14 _____

15 Which property is illustrated by the equation
−4 + 4 = 0?

    A Additive Identity Property

    B Property of Additive Inverses

    C Associative Property

    D Commutative Property

15 _____

16 How many terms are in the algebraic expression below?

$$4x − 2y + 3$$

    F 2   **H** 5

    G 3   **J** 7

16 _____

17 $\dfrac{12a^2b^3c^6}{2bc^3} =$

    A $6a^2b^2c^3$ **C** $6a^2b^3c^{18}$

    B $6a^2b^3c^2$ **D** $6a^2b^4c^9$

17 _____

18 Which is the graph of $y = -2x^2$?

18 _____

F
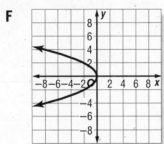

H
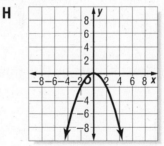

G
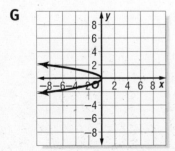

J
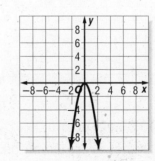

19 What is the slope of the line shown below?

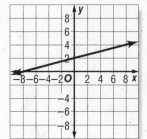

A $\frac{1}{4}$ **B** $\frac{1}{2}$ **C** 2   **D** 4

20 Which is the graph of $y = -3x - 2$?

F
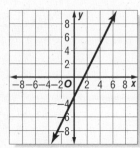

H
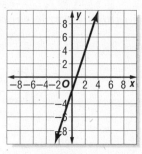

G
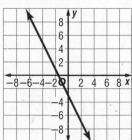

J
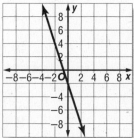

21 Which relationship is best shown by the graph below?

A Oranges cost $0.50 per pound.

B A tree grows 2 inches every 5 months.

C The temperature of a cooler decreases 4 degrees every 10 minutes that it is open.

D A pool's water level increases at 5 gallons per minute.

22 Solve for x.
$$12 - 14x = -72$$

    F −36   **H** 6
    G −6   **J** 36

22 _____

23 Joe ran 1.5 miles in 12 minutes. If Joe runs at the same rate, how long will it take him to run a 10-mile race?

    A 75 minutes   **C** 102 minutes
    B 80 minutes   **D** 180 minutes

23 _____

24 The table below describes the typing speeds of four students.

24 _____

Student	Results of Timed Test
Ansel	85 words every 2 minutes
Lisa	18 words every 30 seconds
Tyrone	33 words every 45 seconds

List the students in order from least to greatest typing speed.

    F Lisa, Ansel, Tyrone
    G Lisa, Tyrone, Ansel
    H Tyrone, Ansel, Lisa
    J Ansel, Tyrone, Lisa

25 The length of a rectangle is 3 times the width. The perimeter is 48 centimeters. What is the area?

    A 108 cm^2 **C** 222.75 cm^2
    B 141.75 cm^2 **D** 432 cm^2

25 _____

26 The hypotenuse of a right triangle is 4 meters long. One leg is 3 meters long. What is the length of the other leg?

    F $\sqrt{7}$ meters   **H** 3.5 meters
    G $\sqrt{12}$ meters   **J** 5 meters

26 _____

27 Quadrilateral *ABCD* is congruent to quadrilateral *PQRS*.

27 _____

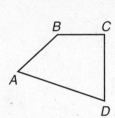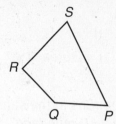

Which statement is true?

A $\overline{AB} \cong \overline{QR}$ **C** $\angle D \cong \angle P$

B $\overline{AB} \cong \overline{PQ}$ **D** $\angle D \cong \angle R$

28 The figure below is a rectangular prism.

28 _____

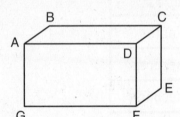

Which word describes the lines containing edges $\overline{AB}$ and $\overline{DF}$?

F parallel   **H** intersecting
G perpendicular   **J** skew

29 Mr. Thompson displayed his students' test results in the stem-and-leaf plot below. How many students' scores are displayed?

29 _____

Stem	Leaf
9	3 6 6 8
8	0 4 7
7	0 0 5 8 9
4	5 8

A 4   **B** 11   **C** 14   **D** 18

30 The list below shows the number of hours each member of a club spent volunteering one month. What is the median of the data?

30 _____

12, 7, 4.5, 9, 7, 11, 13, 12.5

F 7   **G** 8   **H** 9.5   **J** 10

Placement Test
Scoring Guide
Geometry

Student Name _____

For each part, mark the box under the number of correctly answered questions.

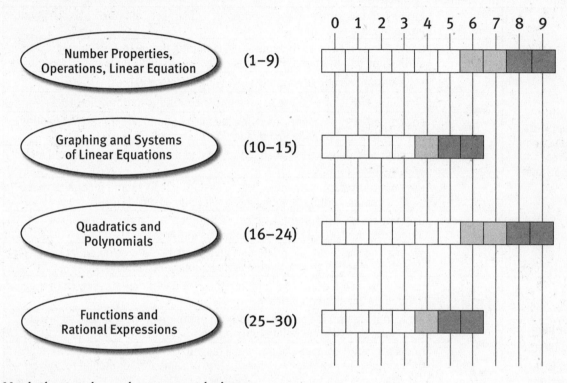

		0	1	2	3	4	5	6	7	8	9
Number Properties, Operations, Linear Equation	(1–9)										
Graphing and Systems of Linear Equations	(10–15)										
Quadratics and Polynomials	(16–24)										
Functions and Rational Expressions	(25–30)										

Mark the total number correct below.

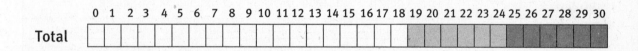

Total 0 1 2 3 4 5 6 7 8 9 10 11 12 13 14 15 16 17 18 19 20 21 22 23 24 25 26 27 28 29 30

Key: Consider this student for...

☐ *California Algebra 1: Concepts, Skills, and Problem Solving*

▨ Geometry Remediation Ancillary—See page 92 for materials list.

▨ Geometry

Student Name _____

In the column on the left, mark the questions that the student answered *incorrectly*.

Strand	May Need Intervention	Objective
Number Properties, Operations, Linear Equations	☐ 1	identify and use the arithmetic properties of subsets of integers and rational, irrational, and real numbers
	☐ 2	understand and use such operations as finding the reciprocal, taking a root, and raising to a fractional power; use the rules of exponents
	☐ 3	solve equations and inequalities involving absolute values
	☐ 4	simplify expressions before solving linear equations in one variable
	☐ 5	solve multi-step problems involving linear equations and linear inequalities in one variable and provide justification for each step
	☐ 6	explain the difference between inductive and deductive reasoning and identify and provide examples of each
	☐ 7	use counterexamples to show that an assertion is false and recognize that a single counterexample is sufficient to refute an assertion
	☐ 8	use properties of numbers to construct simple, valid arguments for, or formulate counterexamples to, claimed assertions
	☐ 9	given a specific algebraic statement involving absolute value equations, determine whether the statement is true sometimes, always, or never
Graphing and Systems of Linear Equations	☐ 10	graph a linear equation and compute the x- and y-intercepts; sketch the region defined by linear inequalities
	☐ 11 ☐ 12	verify that a point lies on a line, given an equation of the line; derive linear equations by using the point-slope formula
	☐ 13	understand the concepts of parallel lines and perpendicular lines and how their slopes are related; find the equation of a line perpendicular to a given line that passes through a given point
	☐ 14 ☐ 15	solve a system of two linear equations in two variables algebraically and interpret the answer graphically; solve a set of two linear inequalities in two variables and sketch the solution sets
Quadratics and Polynomials	☐ 16	add, subtract, multiply, and divide monomials and polynomials; solve multi-step problems by using these techniques
	☐ 17	apply basic factoring techniques to second- and simple third-degree polynomials
	☐ 18 ☐ 19	solve a quadratic equation by factoring or completing the square
	☐ 20	know the quadratic formula and know its proof by completing the square
	☐ 21 ☐ 22	use the quadratic formula to find the roots of a second-degree polynomial and solve quadratic equations
	☐ 23	graph quadratic functions and know that their roots are the x-intercepts
	☐ 24	apply quadratic equations to physical problems
Functions and Rational Expressions	☐ 25	simplify fractions with polynomials in the numerator and denominator by factoring both and reduce them to the lowest terms
	☐ 26 ☐ 27	add, subtract, multiply, and divide rational expressions and functions
	☐ 28	apply algebraic techniques to solve percent mixture problems
	☐ 29	understand the concepts of a function, determine whether a given relation defines a function
	☐ 30	determine the domain of independent variables

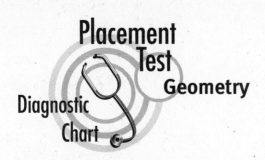

Placement Test
Geometry
Diagnostic Chart

Student Performance Level	Number of Questions Correct	Suggestions for Intervention and Remediation
Intensive Intervention	0–16	Use *California Algebra 1: Concepts, Skills, and Problem Solving* to accelerate the achievement of students who are below grade level. Students should follow a personalized remediation plan. A variety of materials and instructional methods are recommended. For example, instruction and practice should be provided in print, technology, and hands-on lessons.
Strategic Intervention	17–22	Use the additional Intervention and Remediation materials listed on the next page. This list of materials can provide helpful resources for students who struggle in the traditional mathematics program. Strategic intervention allows students to continue to remain in the *California Mathematics: Concepts, Skills, and Problem Solving* program, while receiving the differentiated instruction they need. Teaching Tips and other resources are also listed in the Teacher Wraparound Edition.
Geometry	23 or more	Use *California Geometry: Concepts, Skills, and Problem Solving*. This student does not require overall intervention. However, based on the student's performance on the different sections, intervention may be required. For example, a student who missed 6 or more questions in the Quadratics and Polynomials section may require extra assistance as you cover these skills throughout the year.

A Special Note About Intervention

When using diagnostic tests, teachers should always question the reason behind the students' scores. Students can struggle with mathematics concepts for a variety of reasons. Personalized instruction is recommended for English language learners, students with specific learning disabilities, students with certain medical conditions, or for those who struggle with traditional instructional practice. Teachers should always consider the needs of the individual student when determining the best approach for instruction and program placement.

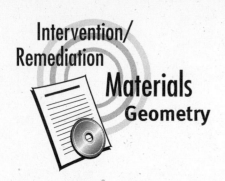

Intervention/Remediation Materials
Geometry

Print Materials

Quick Review Math Handbook	A comprehensive reference of important mathematical terms and concepts to help build math literacy. Also available in Spanish.
Study Guide and Intervention Masters	A brief explanation, along with examples and exercises, for every lesson in the Student Edition. These masters are included in the Chapter Resource Masters.
Skills Practice Masters	Additional practice in computational and application exercises for each lesson in the Student Edition. These masters are included in the Chapter Resource Masters.
Practice Masters	Additional practice in computational and spiral review exercises for each lesson in the Student Edition. These masters are included in the Chapter Resource Masters.
Study Guide and Intervention Workbook	A consumable version of the Study Guide and Intervention Masters for each lesson. Also available in Spanish.
Skills Practice Workbook	A consumable version of the Skills Practice Workbook Masters for each lesson. Also available in Spanish.
Practice Workbook	A consumable version of the Practice Masters for each lesson. Also available in Spanish.
Prerequisite Skills Workbook: Remediation and Intervention	Arithmetic study guide and practice pages for each of the prerequisite skills that review basic math concepts. Also available in Spanish.

Technology Products

ExamView Pro® Assessment Suite	Networkable software includes a Worksheet Builder to make worksheets and tests, a Student Module to take tests on-screen, and a Management System to keep student records.
Mathematics Super DVDs	Includes: MindJogger Plus, a chapter review provided in a game-show format, and What's Math Got to Do With It? Real Life Math Videos that show students how math is used in everyday situations through engaging videos.
Problem-Solving Practice Masters	Additional practice in application exercises for each lesson in the Student Edition.

Diagnostic and Placement
Geometry

Name _____

Date _____

This test contains 30 multiple-choice questions. Work each problem in the space on this page. Select the best answer. Write the letter of the answer on the blank at the right.

1 Which expression is equivalent to $-\frac{1}{2}\left(8 - \frac{1}{2}\right)$?

    A $-4 + \frac{1}{4}$ **C** $7\frac{1}{2} + \frac{1}{4}$

    B $-4 - 1$ **D** $7\frac{1}{2} - 1$

1 _____

2 Simplify $\dfrac{\sqrt{a} \cdot b^2}{a^{\frac{3}{2}} b^5}$.

    F $a^{\frac{1}{3}} b^{\frac{2}{5}}$ **H** $\dfrac{1}{ab^3}$

    G $a^{\frac{3}{4}} b^{10}$ **J** $\dfrac{1}{a^{\frac{3}{4}} b^3}$

2 _____

3 What are the solutions to the equation
$$|x - 3| - 8 = -1?$$

    A $x = -5; x = 11$ **C** $x = 7; x = -7$

    B $x = -4; x = 10$ **D** $x = 10; x = -10$

3 _____

4 $2(3x - 1) - 3(x + 5) =$

    F $2x - 17$ **H** $3x - 17$

    G $3x - 16$ **J** $4x + 3$

4 _____

5 Emily is considering two job offers. Company A will pay \$200 per week plus a 6% commission on all sales. Company B will pay \$320 per week plus a 4% commission on all sales. If x represents the dollar amount of sales, which inequality can be solved to find how much Emily will need to sell in a week to earn more by working for Company A?

    A $0.02x > 120$ **C** $0.10x > 120$

    B $0.02x > 520$ **D** $0.10x > 520$

5 _____

6 Which of the following is an example of inductive reasoning?

6 _____

    F Every rectangle is a parallelogram. Every square is a rectangle. Therefore, every square is a parallelogram.

    G If $x > 3$, then $x^2 > y$. Therefore, $4^2 > y$.

    H Ted's bus arrived at his bus stop before 8:05 A.M. every morning for two weeks. Ted decides that his bus will arrive before 8:05 A.M. the next morning.

    J Keisha's uncle promises to give her $5 if she gets a grade of 85 or higher on her math test. Keisha gets a 93 on her math test. Then Keisha's uncle gives her $5.

7 Which of the following is a counterexample that shows the statement $2x \geq x$ is false?

7 _____

    A $x = -1$ **B** $x = 0$ **C** $x = 1$ **D** $x = 2$

8 Which of the following shows a true statement and the correct property to justify that statement?

8 _____

    F $2(x + 8) = 2x + 8$; Distributive Property

    G $2(x + 8) = 2x + 16$; Distributive Property

    H $2(x + 8) = (2x) + 8$; Associative Property

    J $2(x + 8) = (2x) + 16$; Associative Property

9 For what value or values of x is the following statement true?

9 _____

$$\left|x^2 - 1\right| = -\left(x^2 - 1\right)$$

    A only -1 and 1 **C** all negative real numbers

    B all real numbers   **D** no real numbers

10 Which is the graph of $3x - 2y \leq -6$?

10 _____

F

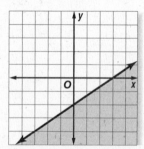

H

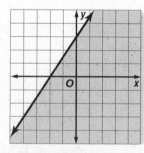

G

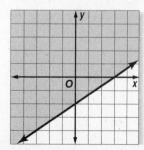

J

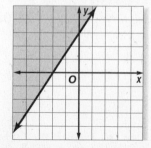

11 Which point lies on the line whose equation is $x - 3y = 6$?

11 _____

   A $(-3, 3)$ **C** $(-3, 9)$

   B $(3, -1)$ **D** $(9, -1)$

12 Which is an equation of the line that has a slope of $-\frac{1}{3}$ and passes through the point $(-5, 2)$?

12 _____

   F $x - 3y = -11$ **H** $x + 3y = 1$

   G $x - 3y = 11$ **J** $x + 3y = 21$

13 Which is an equation of the line that passes through the point $(1, 2)$ and is perpendicular to the line defined by $2x + 5y = 10$?

13 _____

   A $2x + 5y = -12$ **C** $5x - 2y = -1$

   B $2x + 5y = 12$ **D** $5x - 2y = 1$

14 What is the x-coordinate of the solution of the following system of equations?

14 _____

$$2x + y = 3$$
$$3x - 2y = 4$$

   F $x = \frac{1}{7}$ **H** $x = 2$

   G $x = \frac{10}{7}$ **J** $x = 3$

15 Which shows the solution set of the following system of inequalities?

15 _____

$$x - y \leq -1$$
$$x + 2y \leq 0$$

A
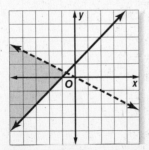

C
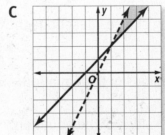

B
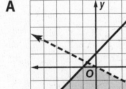

D
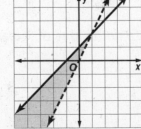

16 $(x - 1)(x - 2) - (x^2 - 1) =$

    F $-2x - 1$ **H** $-3x - 1$

    G $-2x + 1$ **J** $-3x + 3$

16 _____

17 $9x^3 - x =$

    A $x(3x + 1)(3x - 1)$ **C** $x(3x - 1)^2$

    B $x(9x - 1)(x - 1)$ **D** $x(9x - 1)^2$

17 _____

18 What are the solutions to the equation $2x^2 + 9x = 5$?

    F $x = -1, x = \frac{5}{2}$ **H** $x = 5, x = -\frac{1}{2}$

    G $x = 1, x = -\frac{5}{2}$ **J** $x = -5, x = \frac{1}{2}$

18 _____

19 Ray wants to solve the equation $x^2 - 6x + 1 = 0$ by the method of completing the square. His first step is shown below.

$$x^2 - 6x + 1 = 0$$
$$x^2 - 6x \quad\quad = -1$$

Which of the following shows the next step?

    A $x(x - 6) = -1$ **C** $x^2 - 6x - 9 = -1 - 9$

    B $x^2 = 6x - 1$ **D** $x^2 - 6x + 9 = -1 + 9$

19 _____

20 The quadratic formula gives an expression for the solutions to the equation $ax^2 + bx + c = 0$. The first two steps in deriving the quadratic formula are shown below.

$$ax^2 + bx + c = 0$$
$$ax^2 + bx \quad\quad = -c$$
$$x^2 + \frac{b}{a}x \quad\quad = -\frac{c}{a}$$

Which of the following choices describes the next step in deriving the formula?

    F   Add $\frac{b^2}{4a^2}$ to both sides of the equation.

    G   Add $-\frac{b}{2a}$ to both sides of the equation.

    H   Divide both sides of the equation by 2.

    J   Add $\sqrt{b^2 - 4ac}$ to both sides of the equation.

20 _____

21 What are the solutions of the equation $x^2 - 5x - 1 = 0$?

21 _____

    A $\dfrac{-5 + \sqrt{21}}{2}$ and $\dfrac{-5 - \sqrt{21}}{2}$

    B $\dfrac{-5 + \sqrt{29}}{2}$ and $\dfrac{-5 - \sqrt{29}}{2}$

    C $\dfrac{5 + \sqrt{21}}{2}$ and $\dfrac{5 - \sqrt{21}}{2}$

    D $\dfrac{5 + \sqrt{29}}{2}$ and $\dfrac{5 - \sqrt{29}}{2}$

22 Which is a zero (root) of the polynomial $2x^2 - x - 5$?

22 _____

    F $\dfrac{1 - \sqrt{41}}{2}$ **H** $\dfrac{1 - \sqrt{41}}{4}$

    G $\dfrac{-1 + \sqrt{41}}{2}$ **J** $\dfrac{-1 + \sqrt{41}}{4}$

23 An x-intercept of the graph of $y = x^2 - x + c$ is -6. What is the value of c?

23 _____

    A -42 **C** -2

    B -30 **D** 3

24 If an object is thrown upward with an initial velocity of 40 feet per second from a height of 56 feet, its height h is given by the equation $h = -16t^2 + 40t + 56$. In the equation, h is the height in feet and t is the time in seconds after the object is thrown. (Air resistance is neglected.) How many seconds will it take for the object to hit the ground after it is thrown?

24 _____

    F 1 second   **H** 3.5 seconds

    G 3.1 seconds   **J** 7 seconds

25 Simplify $\dfrac{x^2 - 1}{x^2 + x - 2}$.

25 _____

    A $\dfrac{x + 1}{x + 2}$ **C** $\dfrac{x - 1}{x + 2}$

    B $\dfrac{x + 1}{x - 2}$ **D** $\dfrac{x - 1}{x - 2}$

26 $\dfrac{x}{x - 3} + \dfrac{2}{x^2 - 9} =$

26 _____

    F $\dfrac{x + 2}{x^2 + x - 12}$ **H** $\dfrac{x^2 - 3x + 2}{x^2 - 9}$

    G $\dfrac{x^3 - 9x}{2x - 6}$ **J** $\dfrac{x^2 + 3x + 2}{x^2 - 9}$

27 Solve $\frac{1}{x-5} - \frac{3}{x} = \frac{1}{x}$.

A $x = \frac{3}{20}$ **C** $x = \frac{5}{2}$

B $x = \frac{2}{5}$ **D** $x = \frac{20}{3}$

28 Teva has 500 milliliters of a juice drink that is 20% grape juice. She also has some juice drink that is 50% grape juice. How many milliliters of the 50% mixture must she add to 500 milliliters of the 20% mixture to get a mixture that is 25% grape juice?

F 12.5 milliliters   **H** 100 milliliters

G 62.5 milliliters   **J** 150 milliliters

29 Which equation does NOT define y as a function of x?

A $y = x^2$ **C** $x = y^2$

B $y = x + 5$ **D** $x = y + 5$

30 What is the domain of the function $f(x) = \frac{3}{x+2}$?

F the set of all real numbers

G the set of all real numbers except $x = -2$

H the set of all real numbers except $x = 0$

J the set of all real numbers except $x = 2$

Placement Test
Scoring Guide
Algebra 2

Student Name _____

For each part, mark the box under the number of correctly answered questions.

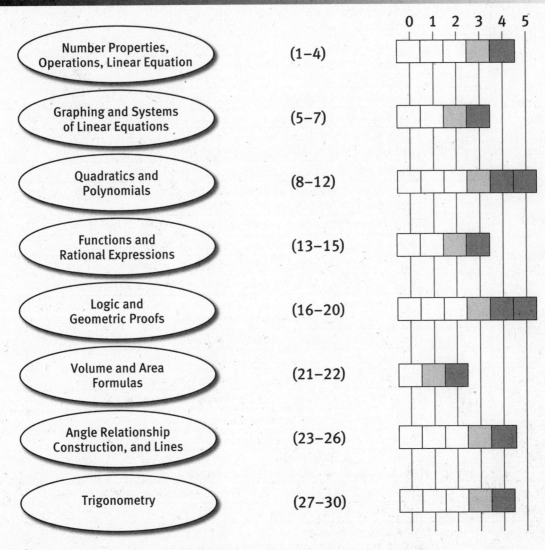

		0 1 2 3 4 5
Number Properties, Operations, Linear Equation	(1–4)	
Graphing and Systems of Linear Equations	(5–7)	
Quadratics and Polynomials	(8–12)	
Functions and Rational Expressions	(13–15)	
Logic and Geometric Proofs	(16–20)	
Volume and Area Formulas	(21–22)	
Angle Relationship Construction, and Lines	(23–26)	
Trigonometry	(27–30)	

Mark the total number correct below.

Total 0 1 2 3 4 5 6 7 8 9 10 11 12 13 14 15 16 17 18 19 20 21 22 23 24 25 26 27 28 29 30

Key: Consider this student for...

☐ *California Geometry: Concepts, Skills, and Problem Solving*

▨ Algebra 2 Remediation Ancillary—See page 102 for materials list.

▦ Algebra 2

Placement Test

Student Name _____

In the column on the left, mark the questions that the student answered *incorrectly*.

Strand	May Need Intervention	Objective
Number Properties, Operations, Linear Equations	☐ 1	understand and use such operations as taking the opposite, finding the reciprocal, taking a root, raising to a fractional power
	☐ 2	solve equations and inequalities involving absolute values
	☐ 3	simplify expressions before solving linear equations and inequalities in one variable, such as $3(2x - 5) + 4(x - 2) = 12$
	☐ 4	solve multistep problems involving linear equations in one variable
Graphing and Systems of Linear Equations	☐ 5	graph a linear equation and compute the x- and y-intercepts
	☐ 6	verify that a point lies on a line, given an equation of the line; derive linear equations by using the point-slope formula
	☐ 7	solve a system of two linear equations in two variables algebraically
Quadratics and Polynomials	☐ 8	add, subtract, multiply, and divide monomials and polynomials; solve multistep problems by using these techniques
	☐ 9	solve a quadratic equation by factoring or completing the square
	☐ 10	know the quadratic formula and its proof by completing the square
	☐ 11	use the quadratic formula to solve quadratic equations
	☐ 12	graph quadratic functions and know roots are the x-intercepts
Functions and Rational Expressions	☐ 13	simplify fractions with polynomials in the numerator and denominator by factoring and reducing them to the lowest terms
	☐ 14	add, subtract, multiply, and divide rational expressions and functions
	☐ 15	apply algebraic techniques to solve rate problems
Logic and Geometric Proofs	☐ 16	identify and give examples of deductive reasoning
	☐ 17	write geometric proofs, including proofs by contradiction
	☐ 18	give counterexamples to disprove a statement
	☐ 19	prove basic theorems involving congruence and similarity
	☐ 20	prove and use theorems involving the properties of parallel lines cut by a transversal, the properties of quadrilaterals, and the properties of circles
Volume and Area Formulas	☐ 21	solve problems involving the volume of common geometric figures
	☐ 22	compute areas of polygons
Angle Relationship, Construction, and Lines	☐ 23	find and use measures of sides and of interior and exterior angles of triangles and polygons to classify figures and solve problems
	☐ 24	prove the Pythagorean theorem
	☐ 25	perform basic constructions with a straightedge and compass, such as angle bisectors, perpendicular bisectors, and parallel lines
	☐ 26	prove theorems using coordinate geometry, including the midpoint of a line segment, the distance formula, and various forms of equations of lines
Trigonometry	☐ 27	know the basic trigonometric functions defined by angles of a right triangle and elementary relationships between them
	☐ 28	use trigonometric functions to solve for an unknown length of a side of a right triangle, given an angle and a length of a side
	☐ 29	solve problems regarding relationships among chords, secants, tangents, inscribed angles, and inscribed and circumscribed polygons of circles
	☐ 30	know the effect of rigid motions on figures in the coordinate plane and space, including rotations, translations, and reflections

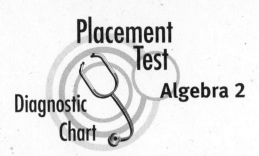

Placement Test
Algebra 2
Diagnostic Chart

Student Performance Level	Number of Questions Correct	Suggestions for Intervention and Remediation
Intensive Intervention	0–5	Use *California Geometry: Concepts, Skills, and Problem Solving* to accelerate the achievement of students who are below grade level. Students should follow a personalized remediation plan. A variety of materials and instructional methods are recommended. For example, instruction and practice should be provided in print, technology, and hands-on lessons.
Strategic Intervention	6–11	Use the additional Intervention and Remediation materials listed on the next page. This list of materials can provide helpful resources for students who struggle in the traditional mathematics program. Strategic intervention allows students to continue to remain in the *California Mathematics: Concepts, Skills, and Problem Solving* program, while receiving the differentiated instruction they need. Teaching Tips and other resources are also listed in the Teacher Wraparound Edition.
Algebra 1	12 or more	Use *California Algebra 2: Concepts, Skills, and Problem Solving*. This student does not require overall intervention. However, based on the student's performance on the different sections, intervention may be required. For example, a student who missed 3 or more questions in the Logic and Geometric Proofs section may require extra assistance as you cover these skills throughout the year.

A Special Note About Intervention

When using diagnostic tests, teachers should always question the reason behind the students' scores. Students can struggle with mathematics concepts for a variety of reasons. Personalized instruction is recommended for English language learners, students with specific learning disabilities, students with certain medical conditions, or for those who struggle with traditional instructional practice. Teachers should always consider the needs of the individual student when determining the best approach for instruction and program placement.

Intervention/Remediation Materials
Algebra 2

Print Materials

Quick Review Math Handbook	A comprehensive reference of important mathematical terms and concepts to help build math literacy. Also available in Spanish.
Study Guide and Intervention Masters	A brief explanation, along with examples and exercises, for every lesson in the Student Edition. These masters are included in the Chapter Resource Masters.
Skills Practice Masters	Additional practice in computational and application exercises for each lesson in the Student Edition. These masters are included in the Chapter Resource Masters.
Practice Masters	Additional practice in computational and spiral review exercises for each lesson in the Student Edition. These masters are included in the Chapter Resource Masters.
Study Guide and Intervention Workbook	A consumable version of the Study Guide and Intervention Masters for each lesson. Also available in Spanish.
Skills Practice Workbook	A consumable version of the Skills Practice Workbook Masters for each lesson. Also available in Spanish.
Practice Workbook	A consumable version of the Practice Masters for each lesson. Also available in Spanish.
Prerequisite Skills Workbook: Remediation and Intervention	Arithmetic study guide and practice pages for each of the prerequisite skills that review basic math concepts. Also available in Spanish.

Technology Products

ExamView Pro® Assessment Suite	Networkable software includes a Worksheet Builder to make worksheets and tests, a Student Module to take tests on-screen, and a Management System to keep student records.
Mathematics Super DVDs	Includes: MindJogger Plus, a chapter review provided in a game-show format, and What's Math Got to Do With It? Real Life Math Videos that show students how math is used in everyday situations through engaging videos.
Problem-Solving Practice Masters	Additional practice in application exercises for each lesson in the Student Edition.

Diagnostic and Placement
Algebra 2

Name _____

Date _____

This test contains 30 multiple-choice questions. Work each problem in the space on this page. Select the best answer. Write the letter of the answer on the blank at the right.

1 Simplify $\left(x^{\frac{1}{2}}\right)^4\left(x^{\frac{1}{2}}\right)\sqrt{xy}$.

    A $x\sqrt{xy}$ **C** $x^3\sqrt{y}$

    B $x^2\sqrt{xy}$ **D** $x^{\frac{11}{2}}\sqrt{y}$

1 _____

2 What are the solutions to the equation $-2|x-3| = -10$?

    F $x = 5; x = -5$ **H** $x = 8; x = -2$

    G $x = 8; x = -8$ **J** no solution

2 _____

3 Simplify the expression $4(2x - 1) - 3(x + 5)$.

    A $3x - 19$ **C** $5x - 19$

    B $5x - 16$ **D** $9x - 2$

3 _____

4 Use the equation $C = \frac{5}{9}(F - 32)$ to convert $11°C$ to Fahrenheit.

    F $-12.2°F$ **H** $38.1°F$

    G $-11.7°F$ **J** $51.8°F$

4 _____

5 Which is the graph of $5x + 3y = 6$?

    A

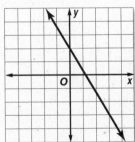

    C

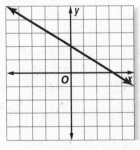

    B

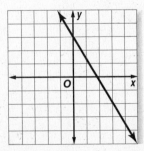

    D

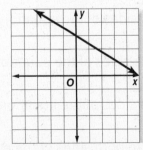

5 _____

6 Which is an equation of the line that has a slope of $\frac{1}{2}$ and passes through the point $(3, -1)$?

6 _____

F $x + 2y = 1$ **H** $x - 2y = 5$

G $x + 2y = -1$ **J** $x - 2y = 8$

7 What is the y-coordinate of the solution of the following system of equations?

7 _____

$$2x - 5y = 0$$
$$x + 2y = -4$$

A $y = -1$ **C** $y = \frac{8}{3}$

B $y = -\frac{8}{9}$ **D** $y = 8$

8 $(x + 2)(x^2 - 1) + x =$

8 _____

F $x^2 + 2x + 1$ **H** $x^3 + x - 2$

G $2x^2 + 2x - 2$ **J** $x^3 + 2x^2 - 2$

9 What are the solutions to the equation $3x^2 + 11x = 4$?

9 _____

A $x = -\frac{1}{3}, x = 4$ **C** $x = -\frac{4}{3}, x = 1$

B $x = \frac{1}{3}, x = -4$ **D** $x = \frac{4}{3}, x = -1$

10 The quadratic formula gives an expression for the solutions to the equation $ax^2 + bx + c = 0$. The first two steps in deriving the quadratic formula are shown below.

10 _____

$$ax^2 + bx + c = 0$$
$$ax^2 + bx = -c$$
$$x^2 + \frac{b}{a}x = -\frac{c}{a}$$

Which of the following choices describes the next step in deriving the formula?

F Add $\frac{b^2}{4a^2}$ to both sides of the equation.

G Add $-\frac{b}{2a}$ to both sides of the equation.

H Add $-b$ to both sides of the equation.

J Add $\sqrt{b^2 - 4ac}$ to both sides of the equation.

11 What are the solutions of the equation $x^2 - 3x - 1 = 0$?

A $\dfrac{-3 + \sqrt{5}}{2}$ and $\dfrac{-3 - \sqrt{5}}{2}$ **C** $\dfrac{3 + \sqrt{5}}{2}$ and $\dfrac{3 - \sqrt{5}}{2}$

B $\dfrac{-3 + \sqrt{13}}{2}$ and $\dfrac{-3 - \sqrt{13}}{2}$ **D** $\dfrac{3 + \sqrt{13}}{2}$ and $\dfrac{3 - \sqrt{13}}{2}$

12 Which is the graph of $y = (x + 3)(x - 1)$?

F
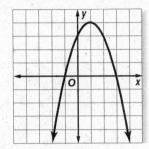

H
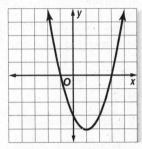

G
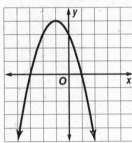

J
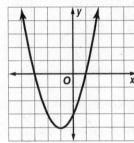

13 Simplify $\dfrac{x^2 - 2x - 3}{x^2 - 9}$.

A $\dfrac{x + 1}{x + 3}$ **C** $\dfrac{x + 1}{x - 3}$

B $\dfrac{x - 1}{x + 3}$ **D** $\dfrac{x - 3}{x - 9}$

14 Solve $\dfrac{3}{2x - 1} + \dfrac{1}{x} = \dfrac{5}{x}$.

F $x = \dfrac{5}{11}$ **H** $x = \dfrac{5}{4}$

G $x = \dfrac{4}{5}$ **J** $x = \dfrac{11}{5}$

15 It takes 20 minutes to fill a barrel using a small hose.
It takes 12 minutes to fill the barrel using a large hose.
How long would it take to fill the barrel using both hoses?

A 7.5 minutes   **C** 12.5 minutes
B 8 minutes   **D** 16 minutes

16 Which of the following is an example of valid deductive reasoning?

    F If Ella does her chores, she gets paid. Ella did not do her chores. Therefore, Ella will not get paid.

    G If Ella does her chores, she gets paid. Ella did not get paid. Therefore, Ella did not do her chores.

    H If the bus is full, then Jim must walk to school. Jim walked to school. Therefore, the bus was full.

    J If the bus is full, then Jim must walk to school. The bus was not full. Therefore, Jim rode the bus to school.

17 Look at the figure below.

Which of the following statements explains why $x = 45$?

    A Base angles of an isosceles triangle are congruent.

    B The sum of the measures of the angles of a triangle is 180°.

    C A diagonal of a square forms an isosceles right triangle.

    D A diagonal of a rectangle forms a right triangle.

18 Which of the following is a counterexample that disproves the statement $x^2 \geq x$?

    F $x = -0.5$ **G** $x = 0.5$ **H** $x = 1.0$ **J** $x = 1.5$

19 In the figure below, it is given that $\overline{BC}$ is parallel to $\overline{AD}$.

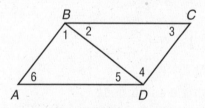

Which of the following can you conclude?

    A Angles 1 and 4 are congruent.

    B Angles 2 and 5 are congruent.

    C Angles 3 and 4 are congruent.

    D Angles 3 and 6 are congruent.

20 The radius of the circle below is 5 centimeters. Line segment *AB* is a diameter of the circle. What is the value of *x*, to the nearest tenth?

20 _____

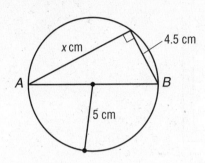

F 6.7   **G** 7.3   **H** 8.9   **J** 9.5

21 The volume of a cone is given by the formula $V = \frac{1}{3}\pi r^2 h$. What is the volume of the cone below, to the nearest whole number? Use 3.14 for π.

21 _____

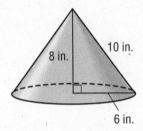

A 100 cubic inches   **C** 301 cubic inches
B 126 cubic inches   **D** 377 cubic inches

22 Ed needs to paint the front wall on the building shown below. What is the area of the wall?

22 _____

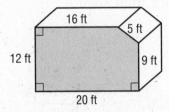

F 216 square feet   **H** 244 square feet
G 234 square feet   **J** 260 square feet

23 Mya is making a frame for a window. She has already measured two edges as shown. Now she wants to make sure all the angles are right angles.

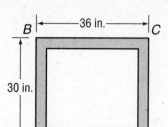

Which of the following can Mya do to make sure that all the angles are right angles?

A Make the diagonal distances *AC* and *BD* equal.

B Make the diagonal distance *AC* = 40 inches.

C Make the diagonal distance *BD* = 40 inches.

D Make *AD* = 36 inches and *CD* = 30 inches.

24 In the right triangle below, *M* is the midpoint of hypotenuse *QR*.

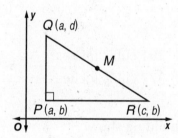

Which expression represents the distance from point *P* to point *M*?

F $\left(\frac{a+c}{2}\right) + \left(\frac{d+b}{2}\right)$

H $\left(\frac{c-a}{2}\right) + \left(\frac{b-d}{2}\right)$

G $\sqrt{\left(\frac{a+c}{2}\right)^2 + \left(\frac{d+b}{2}\right)^2}$

J $\sqrt{\left(\frac{c-a}{2}\right)^2 + \left(\frac{d-b}{2}\right)^2}$

25 Cary was given the figure below on the left. He used a compass and straightedge to construct the line through point *P* perpendicular to line m. The diagram below shows his work.

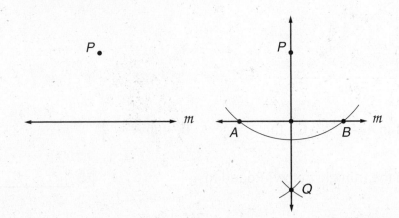

To prove the construction is correct, Cary can draw additional line segments on the figure and show that triangle *PAQ* is congruent to triangle *PBQ*. Which triangle congruence property can he use to justify that the triangles are congruent, based on his method of construction?

A SSS (If three sides of one triangle are congruent to three sides of another triangle, then the triangles are congruent.)

B SAS (If two sides and the included angle of one triangle are congruent to two sides and the included angle of another triangle, then the triangles are congruent.)

C ASA (If two angles and the included side of one triangle are congruent to two angles and the included side of another triangle, then the triangles are congruent.)

D AAS (If two angles and a side of one triangle are congruent to two angles and a side of another triangle, then the triangles are congruent.)

26 In right triangle *ABC* below, $\overline{CD}$ is the altitude to the hypotenuse, *a* is the length of $\overline{BC}$, *b* is the length of $\overline{AC}$, *c* is the length of $\overline{AB}$, and *e* is the length of $\overline{DB}$.

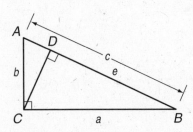

Which ratio equals $\frac{c}{a}$?

F $\frac{e}{a}$ 　　　　**G** $\frac{e}{b}$ 　　　　**H** $\frac{a}{b}$ 　　　　**J** $\frac{a}{e}$

27 For the right triangle shown below, what is the tangent of angle *A*?

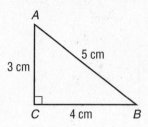

A $\tan A = \frac{3}{4}$ **B** $\tan A = \frac{4}{5}$ **C** $\tan A = \frac{5}{4}$ **D** $\tan A = \frac{4}{3}$

28 What is the value of *x* in the triangle below? Round to the nearest tenth.

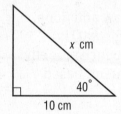

F 11.9   **G** 13.1   **H** 14.1   **J** 15.6

29 The points on the outside of the clock face below are at 12:00, 5:00, and 9:00.

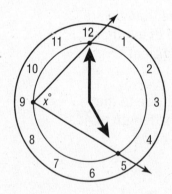

What is the value of *x*?

A 25   **B** 50   **C** 75   **D** 90

30 The triangle shown below is reflected over $\overline{AC}$. Then the image of the reflection is translated 3 units to the left. What are the coordinates of the final image of point *B* after both transformations?

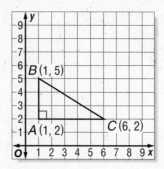

F $(-2, -1)$ **G** $(-2, 0)$ **H** $(1, -4)$ **J** $(1, -8)$

Answers (Grade K)

Diagnostic and Placement
Grade K

Name _____
Date _____

This test contains 15 questions. Work each problem in the space on this page. Select the best answer. Write the answer as directed.

1 Count the apples. Write the number. ___7___

2 Put an X on the set of four cherries.

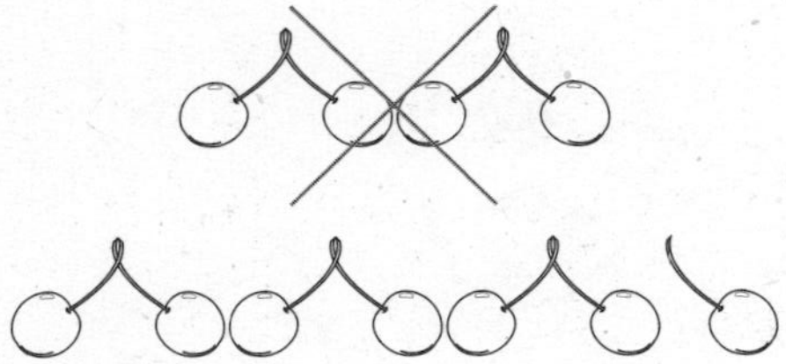

3 Circle the problem that fits the story. $2 + 1 = 3$

$$\begin{array}{r} 2 \\ -1 \\ \hline 1 \end{array}$$

$$\left(\begin{array}{r} 2 \\ +1 \\ \hline 3 \end{array}\right)$$

4 Look at the first square. Circle the squares that are the same size.

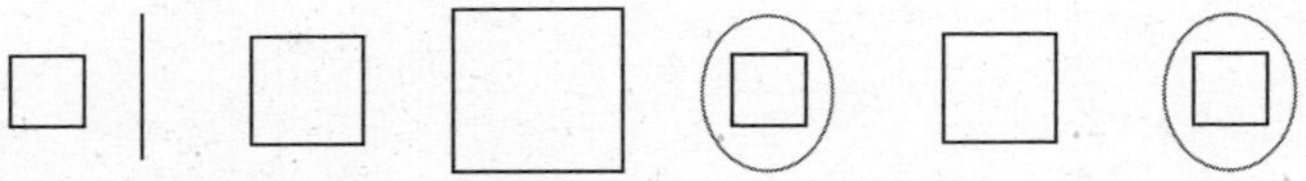

5 Circle the shape that comes next.

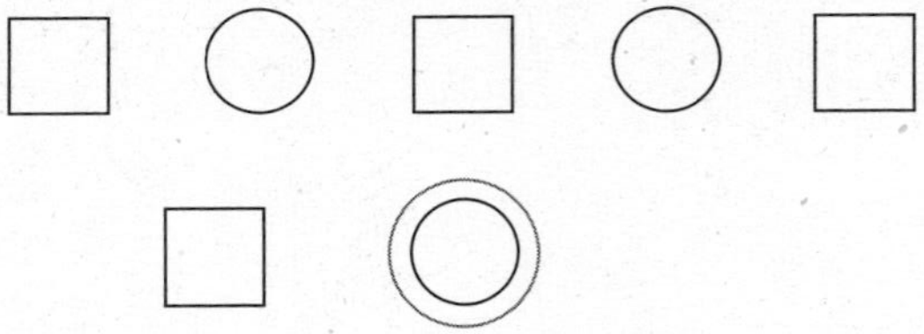

6 Look at the pattern. Circle the part that repeats.

7 Look at the object. Color in the figure that matches the shape of the object.

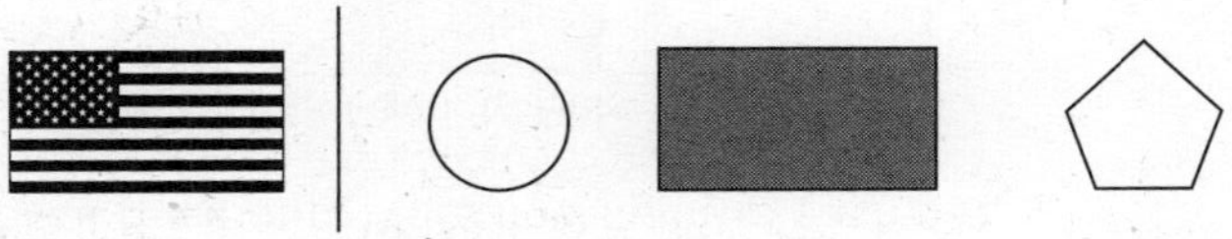

8 Put an X on the objects that can stack.

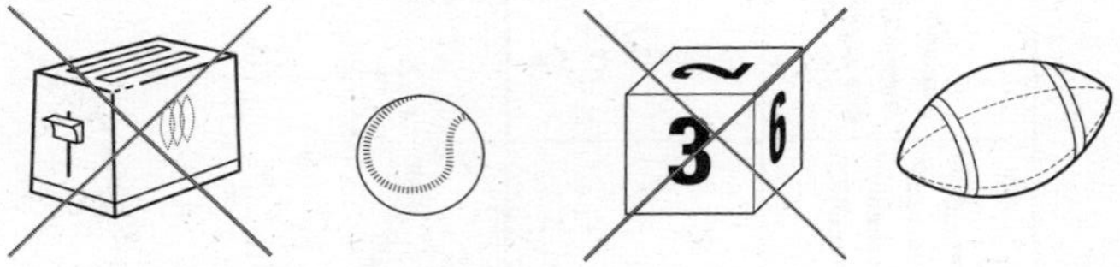

Answers (Grade K)

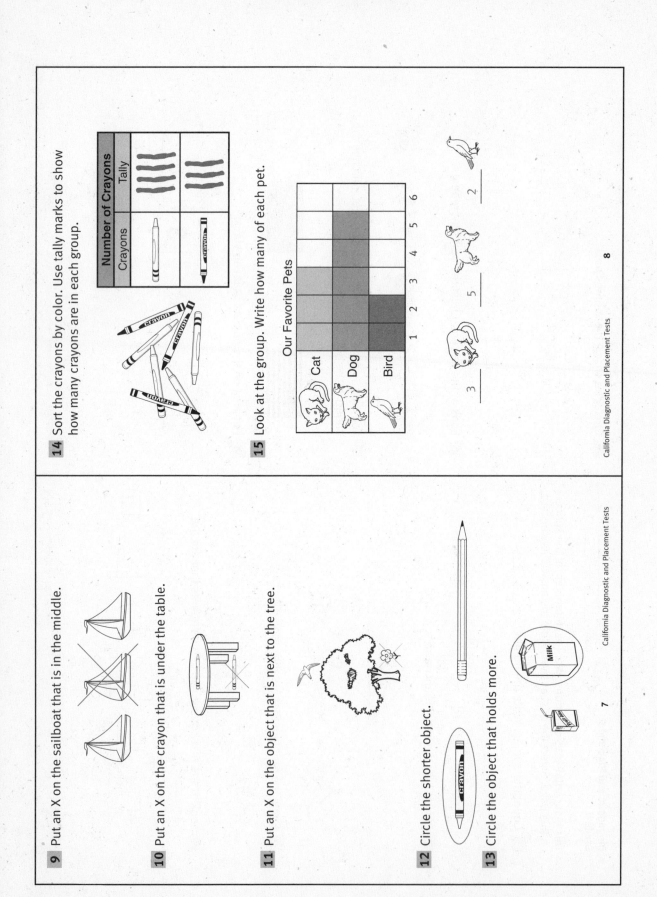

9 Put an X on the sailboat that is in the middle.

10 Put an X on the crayon that is under the table.

11 Put an X on the object that is next to the tree.

12 Circle the shorter object.

13 Circle the object that holds more.

Milk

14 Sort the crayons by color. Use tally marks to show how many crayons are in each group.

Number of Crayons	
Crayons	Tally
crayon	～～～ ～～
CRAYON	～～～ ～～

15 Look at the group. Write how many of each pet.

Our Favorite Pets

	1	2	3	4	5	6
Cat						
Dog						
Bird						

3   5   2

Answers (Grade 1)

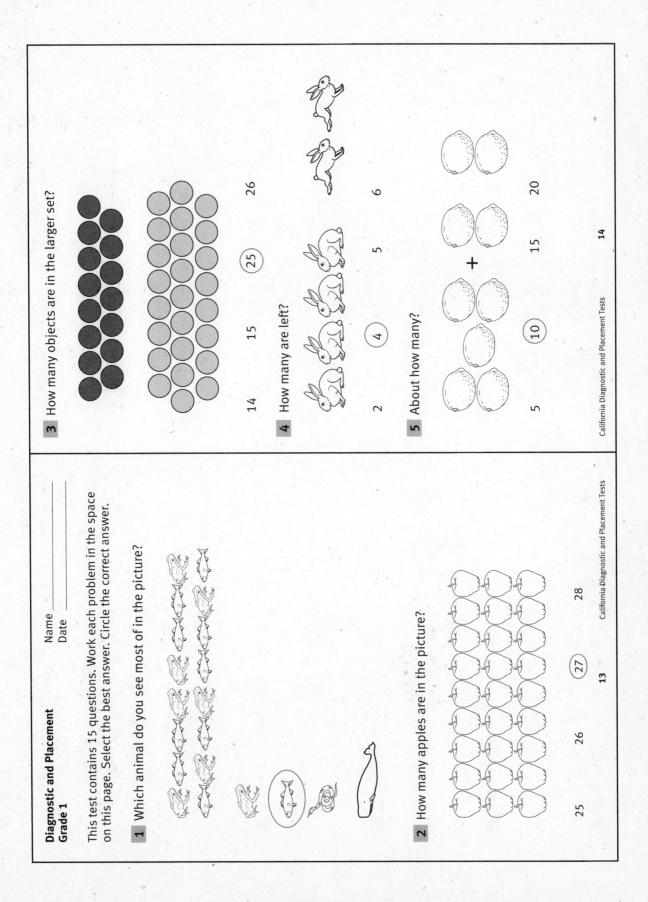

Diagnostic and Placement
Grade 1

Name _____
Date _____

This test contains 15 questions. Work each problem in the space on this page. Select the best answer. Circle the correct answer.

1 Which animal do you see most of in the picture?

2 How many apples are in the picture?

25　　26　　(27)　　28

3 How many objects are in the larger set?

14　　15　　(25)　　26

4 How many are left?

2　　(4)　　5　　6

5 About how many?

+

5　　(10)　　15　　20

Answers (Grade 1)

6 Which object does not belong?

7 Which object does not belong?

8 Which holds more?

9 Which is the heaviest?

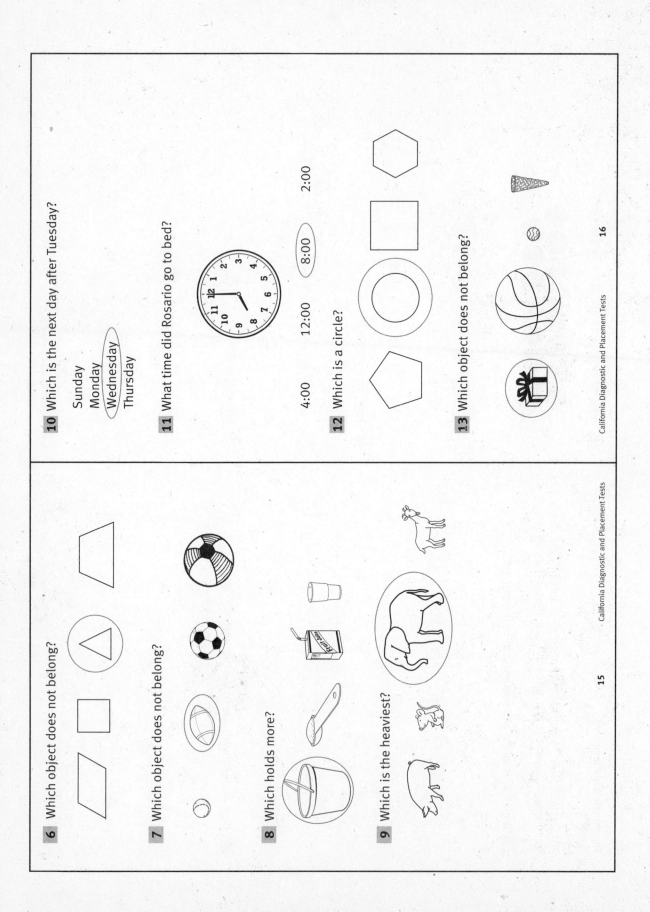

15   California Diagnostic and Placement Tests

10 Which is the next day after Tuesday?

Sunday
Monday
~~Wednesday~~
Thursday

11 What time did Rosario go to bed?

4:00   12:00   8:00   2:00

12 Which is a circle?

13 Which object does not belong?

16   California Diagnostic and Placement Tests

Answers (Grade 1)

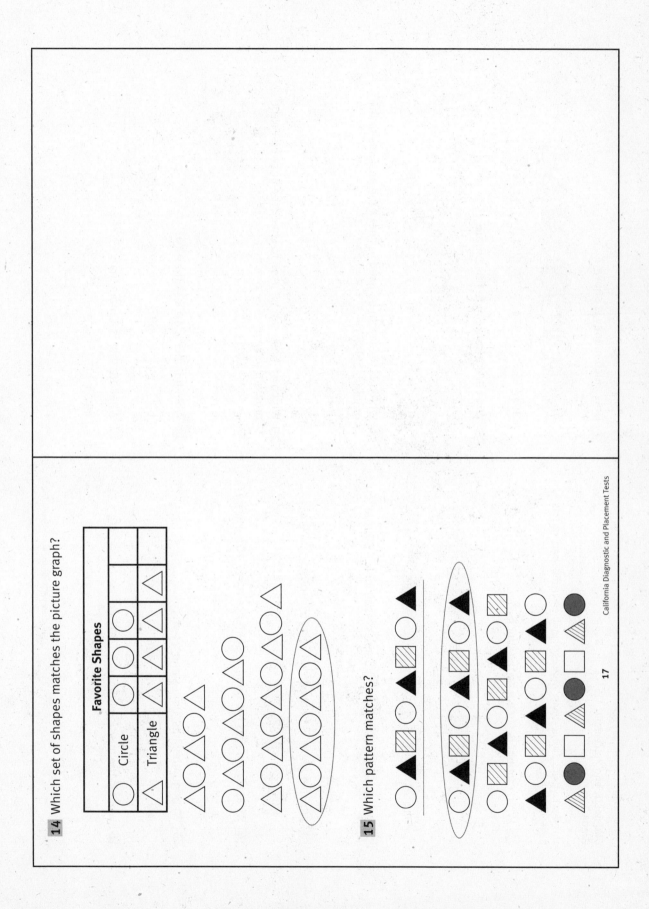

14 Which set of shapes matches the picture graph?

Favorite Shapes

Circle	○	○	○
Triangle	△	△	△

15 Which pattern matches?

California Diagnostic and Placement Tests

17

Answers (Grade 2)

Diagnostic and Placement
Grade 2

Name _____
Date _____

This test contains 30 questions. Work each problem in the space on this page. Circle the best answer.

1 What number is shown by the blocks?

14   60   (68)   86

2 Which sign makes the number sentence 43 ◯ 34 true?

=   (>)   <

+   –

3 Which number is between 68 and 70?

67   (69)   71   72

4 What sign makes the number sentence true? 10 ☐ 6 = 16

(+)   –   ×   =

5 What number has 3 ones and 4 tens?

34   (43)   304   403

6 What is the missing number?   30, 32, 34, ___, 38, 40, 42

33   35   (36)   37

7 How much money is shown?

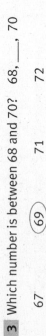

(39¢)   34¢   29¢   24¢

8 What is the solution to this problem?

$$\begin{array}{r} 13 \\ +4 \\ \hline \end{array}$$

8   9   (17)   18

9 Which of these can be used to check the answers to the problem below? $5 + 7 = 12$

$7 + 12 = 19$ $4 + 8 = 12$
$17 - 5 = 12$ $(12 - 7 = 5)$

10 Which of these can be used to check the answers to the problem below? $9 - 6 = 3$

$(3 + 6 = 9)$ $9 + 6 = 15$
$6 - 3 = 3$ $12 - 3 = 9$

11 What number is 10 less than 70?

(60)   69   71   80

12 What number is 1 more than 53?

43   52   (54)   63

Answers (Grade 2)

13 Which number sentence tells how many in all?

⬭ $8 + 6 = 14$
　$4 + 3 = 7$

　$8 - 6 = 2$
　$4 - 3 = 1$

14 Which number sentence tells how many more triangles than squares?

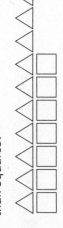

⬭ $11 - 7 =$
　$11 - 4 =$

　$7 + 11 =$
　$7 - 11 =$

15 What is the solution to the problem?

$$\begin{array}{r} 26 \\ + 6 \\ \hline \end{array}$$

14　　21　　22　　㉜

16 What number makes the number sentence true?

$3 + 6 = \square + 5$

3　　④　　5　　6

17 About how many linking cubes can you hold in one hand?

⬭ About 5　　About 500
　About 50　　About 5,000

18 There are 6 baseballs. Eric tossed 2 of them. Which number sentence shows how many are left?

⬭ $6 - 2 = 4$
　$2 + 6 = 8$

　$6 - 4 = 2$
　$2 + 4 = 6$

19 Which number sentence matches the picture?

⬭ $5 + 3 =$
　$8 + 3 =$

　$5 - 3 =$
　$8 - 3 =$

20 Circle the longest object.

21 What time is shown on the clock?

⬭ 2:30　　3:30　　6:15　　7:15

22 Which shape is a triangle?

Answers (Grade 2)

23 Which of the figures has 4 corners and 4 sides?

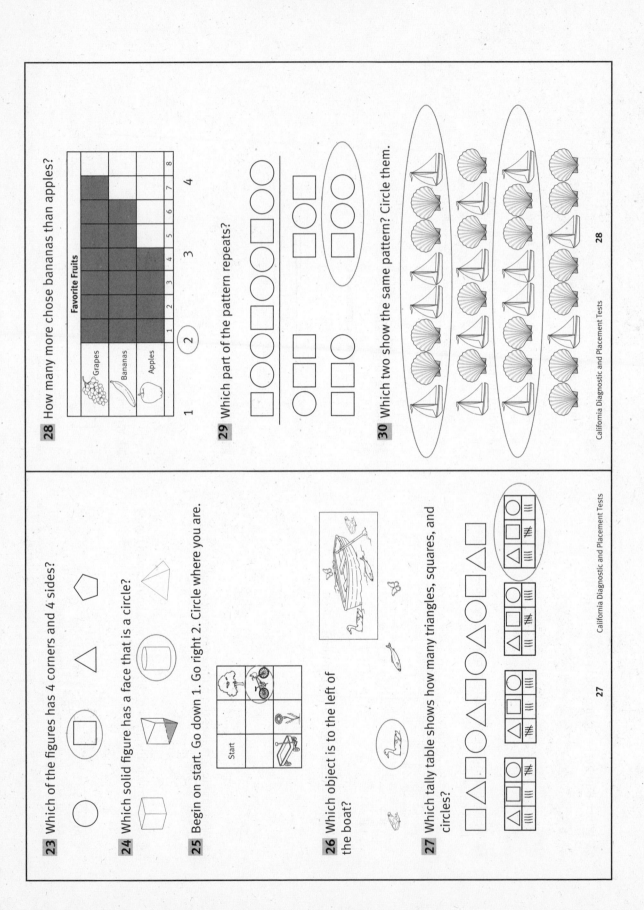

24 Which solid figure has a face that is a circle?

25 Begin on start. Go down 1. Go right 2. Circle where you are.

26 Which object is to the left of the boat?

27 Which tally table shows how many triangles, squares, and circles?

28 How many more chose bananas than apples?

Favorite Fruits

29 Which part of the pattern repeats?

30 Which two show the same pattern? Circle them.

Answers (Grade 3)

Diagnostic and Placement
Grade 3

Name _____

Date _____

This test contains 30 multiple-choice questions. Work each problem in the space on this page. Select the best answer. Write the letter of the answer on the blank at the right.

1 A number has three ones, two tens, and seven hundreds. What is the number?

A 273   B 327   C 723   D 732

1 ___ C

2 What is another way to write five hundred sixty-four?

F $500 + 6 + 4$ H $500 + 60 + 4$
G $5 + 6 + 4$ J $560 + 40$

2 ___ H

3 Which number sentence is true?

A $625 < 671$ C $625 < 625$
B $625 > 641$ D $625 > 714$

3 ___ A

4 Juan did this addition problem. Which problem shows he got the right answer? $6 + 2 = 8$

F $3 + 5 = 8$ H $6 - 2 = 4$
G $8 + 2 = 10$ J $8 - 2 = 6$

4 ___ J

5

$$\begin{array}{r} 244 \\ + 38 \\ \hline \end{array}$$

A 372   B 282   C 272   D 216

5 ___ B

6 Which drawing shows 6×4?

F   G   H   J

6 ___ G

7 Which of the following fractions is the least?

A $\frac{1}{2}$ B $\frac{1}{4}$ C $\frac{1}{9}$ D $\frac{1}{12}$

7 ___ D

33

California Diagnostic and Placement Tests

---

8 There are eight tables at the restaurant. There are two chairs at each table. How many chairs are there altogether?

8   2

F 10   G 16   H 24   J 28

8 ___ G

9 Nina has these crayons. She will put six crayons in each of three boxes. How many crayons will be left out of the boxes?

A 1   B 2   C 3   D 4

9 ___ B

10 Which of the following fractions is the greatest?

F $\frac{1}{3}$ G $\frac{1}{4}$ H $\frac{1}{8}$ J $\frac{1}{10}$

10 ___ F

11 Which fraction is equal to one whole?

A $\frac{5}{5}$ B $\frac{2}{3}$ C $\frac{3}{8}$ D $\frac{1}{4}$

11 ___ A

12 What fraction of the group of animals is cows?

F $\frac{5}{2}$ G $\frac{2}{3}$ H $\frac{3}{5}$ J $\frac{2}{5}$

12 ___ G

13 Tyler has three quarters, five dimes, and one nickel in his piggy bank. How much money does he have?

A $1.10   B $1.25   C $1.30   D $1.60

13 ___ C

34

California Diagnostic and Placement Tests

121   California Diagnostic and Placement Tests

Answers (Grade 3)

14 What is another way to write fifty-two cents?
52¢

F $52   G 52$ H $50.2   J $0.52

14 _____ J

15 Look at the graph. How many books did they read altogether?

Books Read

Jaden	📖📖📖📖📖
Tori	📖📖📖
Andy	📖📖

📖 = 2 books

A 11   B 12   C 16   D 32

15 _____ D

16 What number goes in the box to make this number sentence true?

$18 + 6 = \square + 18$

F 6   G 12   H 18   J 24

16 _____ F

17 Look at the addition problem in the box. Which problem below has the same answer?

$$7 + 4 + 5 = 16$$

A $16 + 5 + 4 =$ C $6 + 3 + 4 =$
B $7 + 4 + 16 =$ D $5 + 7 + 4 =$

17 _____ D

18 Ellie had 26 stickers. Rick gave her some stickers. Now she has 41. Which number sentence could be used to find how many stickers Rick gave Ellie?

F $\square - 41 = 26$ H $\square + 41 = 26$
G $26 - \square = 41$ J $26 + \square = 41$

18 _____ J

35 California Diagnostic and Placement Tests

19 There are 213 third graders and 251 fourth graders. Which number sentence can be used to find how many more fourth graders there are than third graders?

A $213 - 251 = \square$ C $251 - 213 = \square$
B $213 + 251 = \square$ D $251 + 213 = \square$

19 _____ C

20 Look at the picture of the pencil. Measure the length of the pencil in inches. About how many inches long is the pencil?

F 3   G 4   H 5   J 6

20 _____ G

21 Measure the length of the ribbon in centimeters. About how long is the ribbon?

A 8 centimeters   C 10 centimeters
B 9 centimeters   D 11 centimeters

21 _____ C

22 Peter has basketball practice one time every week. How many times does he have basketball practice in one year?

F 24   G 52   H 60   J 365

22 _____ G

23 A movie started at 6:00 P.M. and lasted two hours. When did the movie end?

A 4:00 P.M.   B 7:00 P.M.   C 8:00 P.M.   D 9:00 P.M.

23 _____ C

24 How many faces does this pyramid have?

F 8   G 5   H 4   J 3

24 _____ G

36 California Diagnostic and Placement Tests

Answers (Grade 3)

25 Look at the two triangles. Which of the following shapes could be made from the two triangles?

A

B

C

D

25 _____ C

26 One starfish has five arms, two have ten arms, and three have fifteen arms. How many arms do four starfish have?

F 15   G 20   H 25   J 30

26 _____ G

27 The tally chart shows the number of stars each student earned. Which graph matches the data in the tally chart?

Stars Earned	
Name	Tally
Nick	|||
Grace	卌
Faith	||||
Ben	卌|

A

B

C

D

27 _____ A

28 The bar graph shows the number of students who voted for each color. Which tally chart matches the data in the bar graph?

F

G

H

J

28 _____ G

29 Which age occurs most often?

Students Ages	
Student	Age
Jenny	8
Mandy	10
Eddie	8
Carlos	7
Ross	10
Vicky	8

A 3   B 7   C 8   D 10

29 _____ C

30 Five tricycles have fifteen wheels, four have twelve wheels, and three have nine wheels. How many wheels do two tricycles have?

F 18   G 15   H 6   J 3

30 _____ H

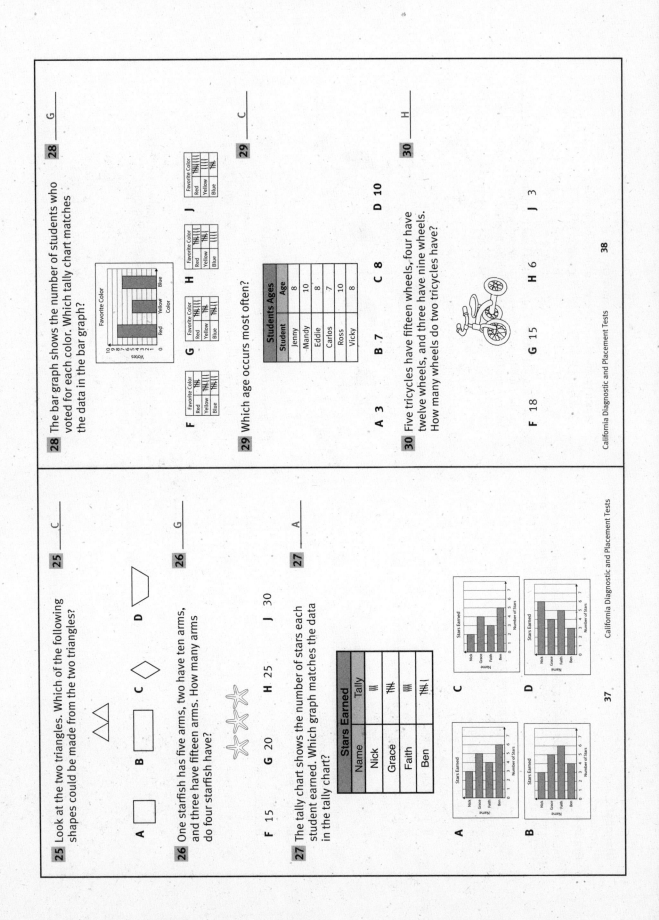

Answers (Grade 4)

Diagnostic and Placement

Grade 4

Name _____
Date _____

This test contains 30 multiple-choice questions. Work each problem in the space on this page. Select the best answer. Write the letter of the answer on the blank at the right.

1 Which set of numbers is in order from least to greatest?

A 895, 924, 862, 941
B 862, 895, 924, 941
C 924, 941, 862, 895
D 941, 924, 895, 862

1 ___B___

2 Which number has a 7 in the ones place and a 2 in the hundreds place?

F 2437   G 3274   H 4237   J 4732

2 ___H___

3 The school auditorium seats 2870 people. Which of these equals 2870?

A $2 + 8 + 70$
B $200 + 80 + 7$
C $2000 + 800 + 70$
D $2000 + 800 + 7$

3 ___C___

4 $5718 + 605 =$

F 5313   G 5323   H 6313   J 6323

4 ___J___

5 Which number is 16 less than 740?

A 724   B 734   C 736   D 756

5 ___A___

6 $8 \times 3 =$

F 11   G 16   H 24   J 32

6 ___H___

California Diagnostic and Placement Tests

7 Andrés did the division problem $552 \div 12 = 46$. Which problem could he do to check his answer?

A $46 \div 12 = \square$
B $46 - 12 = \square$
C $46 \times 12 = \square$
D $46 \div 12 = \square$

7 ___C___

8 Each student brought in 4 cans of food to donate to the food bank. There are 285 students. How many cans did the students donate in all?

F 820   G 840   H 1120   J 1140

8 ___J___

9 Inali and his friends ate $\frac{1}{2}$ of a pizza.

9 ___B___

10 Which fractional part of a circle below is equal to $\frac{1}{2}$?

A   B   C   D

10 ___J___

$10 \quad \frac{3}{8} + \frac{1}{2} =$

F $\frac{2}{6}$ G $\frac{4}{10}$ H $\frac{4}{8}$ J $\frac{7}{8}$

11 Desiree drew a rectangle and divided it into 8 equal parts. She colored $\frac{3}{8}$ of the rectangle red, $\frac{2}{8}$ of the rectangle blue, and the rest green. What fraction of the rectangle did Desiree color green?

A $\frac{1}{8}$ B $\frac{3}{8}$ C $\frac{5}{8}$ D $\frac{6}{8}$

11 ___B___

12 Ana bought 3 books, and a marker. She paid with a ten-dollar bill. How much change should she get back?

F $1.45   G $5.95   H $6.75   J $8.55

12 ___F___

California Diagnostic and Placement Tests

Answers (Grade 4)

13 ___ D ___

The menu shows the prices at Lunchtime Cafe. Tina ordered a turkey sandwich, salad, and juice. What was the total cost of her meal?

Lunchtime Cafe

Item	Cost
Turkey Sandwich	$4.50
Ham Sandwich	$4.35
Salad	$2.10
Fruit Cup	$2.50
Juice	$1.90

A $6.60   **B** $7.50   **C** $8.35   **D** $8.50

14 ___ H ___

Drew has 4 sheets of stickers. Each sheet has 12 stickers. Which number sentence shows how to find the total number of stickers Drew has?

F $12 \div 4 = \square$ **H** $12 \times 4 = \square$
G $12 - 4 = \square$ **J** $12 \div 4 = \square$

15 ___ B ___

Which sign goes in the box to make the number sentence true? $36 \square 9 = 27$

A +   **B** −   **C** ×   **D** ÷

16 ___ J ___

If $15 \times 24 \times 8 = 2880$, then what is $8 \times 24 \times 15$?

F 120   **H** 360
G 192   **J** 2880

17 ___ C ___

The table shows the number of crayons in each box. If every box has the same number of crayons, how many crayons will be in 8 boxes?

Number of Boxes	Number of Crayons
1	8
2	16
3	24

A 8   **B** 32   **C** 64   **D** 72

45 California Diagnostic and Placement Tests

18 ___ J ___

If one dog biscuit costs 45¢, how much will 6 dog biscuits cost?

F $0.51   **G** $2.40   **H** $2.51   **J** $2.70

19 ___ C ___

What is the area of this figure?

$\square$ = 1 square unit

A 4 square units   **C** 7 square units
B 6 square units   **D** 8 square units

20 ___ H ___

A classroom is shaped like a rectangle with a length of 30 feet and a width of 24 feet.

30 ft
24 ft

What is the perimeter in feet of the classroom?

F 54 feet   **G** 84 feet   **H** 108 feet   **J** 720 feet

21 ___ B ___

Which of the following would you measure in feet?

A the length of an eraser
B the height of a classmate
C the weight of a book
D the capacity of a bucket

22 ___ F ___

Which best describes this figure?

F pentagon   **G** hexagon   **H** triangle   **J** octagon

46 California Diagnostic and Placement Tests

Answers (Grade 4)

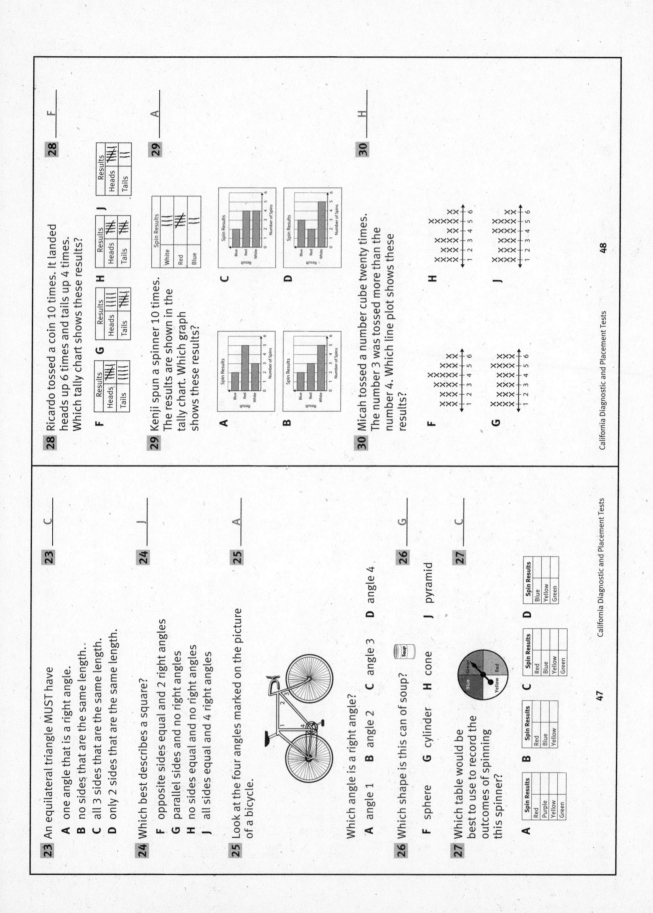

23 An equilateral triangle MUST have
A one angle that is a right angle.
B no sides that are the same length..
C all 3 sides that are the same length.
D only 2 sides that are the same length.

23 _____ C _____

24 Which best describes a square?
F opposite sides equal and 2 right angles
G parallel sides and no right angles
H no sides equal and no right angles
J all sides equal and 4 right angles

24 _____ J _____

25 Look at the four angles marked on the picture of a bicycle.

Which angle is a right angle?
A angle 1   B angle 2   C angle 3   D angle 4

25 _____ A _____

26 Which shape is this can of soup?
F sphere   G cylinder   H cone   J pyramid

26 _____ G _____

27 Which table would be best to use to record the outcomes of spinning this spinner?

A Spin Results: Red / Purple / Yellow / Green
B Spin Results: Red / Blue / Yellow
C Spin Results: Red / Blue / Yellow / Green
D Spin Results: Blue / Yellow / Green

27 _____ C _____

28 Ricardo tossed a coin 10 times. It landed heads up 6 times and tails up 4 times. Which tally chart shows these results?

28 _____ F _____

29 Kenji spun a spinner 10 times. The results are shown in the tally chart. Which graph shows these results?

29 _____ A _____

30 Micah tossed a number cube twenty times. The number 3 was tossed more than the number 4. Which line plot shows these results?

30 _____ H _____

Answers (Grade 5)

Diagnostic and Placement

Grade 5

Name _____

Date _____

This test contains 30 multiple-choice questions. Work each problem in the space on this page. Select the best answer. Write the letter of the answer on the blank at the right.

1 The number 3,040,012 is read as:

A three billion, forty million, twelve

B three million, four thousand, twelve

C three million, forty thousand, twelve

D three hundred four thousand, twelve

1 ____ C

2 Which number is the greatest?

F 13.1   G 5.22   H 2.92   J 1.08

2 ____ F

3 What is 436,708 rounded to the nearest thousand?

A 436,000

B 436,700

C 436,800

D 437,000

3 ____ D

4 Which decimal is equivalent to $\frac{1}{2}$?

F 0.12   G 0.2   H 0.5   J 2.0

4 ____ H

5 Which is the lowest temperature?

A 2°C   B 5°C   C −2°C   D −5°C

5 ____ D

6 Which point could represent 2.34?

F Point A   G Point B   H Point C   J Point D

6 ____ H

7 47,821 − 3,045 =

A 44,776

B 44,786

C 44,824

D 44,876

7 ____ A

8 503 ÷ 4 =

F 13 R1

G 100 R3

H 120 R3

J 125 R3

8 ____ J

9 A school principal bought 46 pizzas for a party. Each pizza was cut into 12 slices. How many slices of pizza were there?

A 138   C 552

B 542   D 638

9 ____ C

10 Ms. Ayala has 54 pencils. She gives the same number of pencils to each of 7 students. She gives out as many pencils as she can. How many pencils does each student get?

F 5   H 7

G 6   J 8

10 ____ H

11 Which has the same value as 6 × 4 × 3?

A 24 × 3

B 18 × 3

C 10 × 3

D 2 × 3

11 ____ A

12 Which is a prime number?

F 7   H 9

G 8   J 10

12 ____ F

Answers (Grade 5)

13 Edmundo had 4 trading cards yesterday. He got some more trading cards today. Now he has 12 trading cards. If n represents the number of trading cards Edmundo got today, which equation is correct?

A $4 + 12 = n$
B $4 + n = 12$
C $n + 12 = 4$
D $n + 4 = 16$

13 ____ B

14 $40 - (10 + 2) =$

F 28   G 32   H 48   J 52

14 ____ F

15 $4 \times (9 - 3) =$

A 48
B 36
C 33
D 24

15 ____ D

16 Which equation below represents the area (A) of the rectangle in square centimeters?

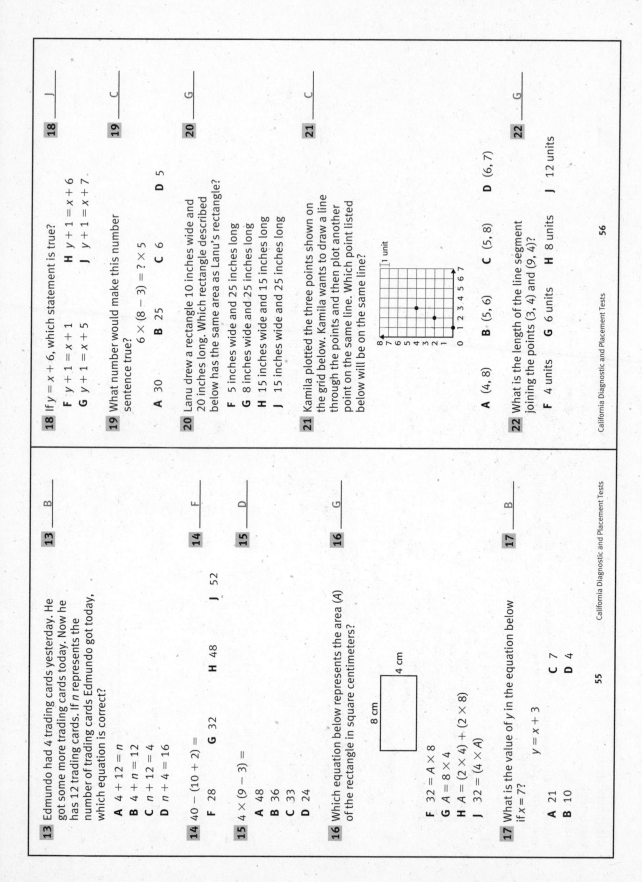

8 cm
4 cm

F $32 = A \times 8$
G $A = 8 \times 4$
H $A = (2 \times 4) + (2 \times 8)$
J $32 = (4 \times A)$

16 ____ G

17 What is the value of y in the equation below if $x = 7$?

$y = x + 3$

A 21
B 10
C 7
D 4

17 ____ B

18 If $y = x + 6$, which statement is true?

F $y + 1 = x + 1$ H $y + 1 = x + 6$
G $y + 1 = x + 5$ J $y + 1 = x + 7$

18 ____ J

19 What number would make this number sentence true?

$6 \times (8 - 3) = ? \times 5$

A 30   B 25   C 6   D 5

19 ____ C

20 Lanu drew a rectangle 10 inches wide and 20 inches long. Which rectangle described below has the same area as Lanu's rectangle?

F 5 inches wide and 25 inches long
G 8 inches wide and 25 inches long
H 15 inches wide and 15 inches long
J 15 inches wide and 25 inches long

20 ____ G

21 Kamila plotted the three points shown on the grid below. Kamila wants to draw a line through the points and then plot another point on the same line. Which point listed below will be on the same line?

1 unit

A $(4, 8)$ B $(5, 6)$ C $(5, 8)$ D $(6, 7)$

21 ____ C

22 What is the length of the line segment joining the points $(3, 4)$ and $(9, 4)$?

F 4 units   G 6 units   H 8 units   J 12 units

22 ____ G

Answers (Grade 5)

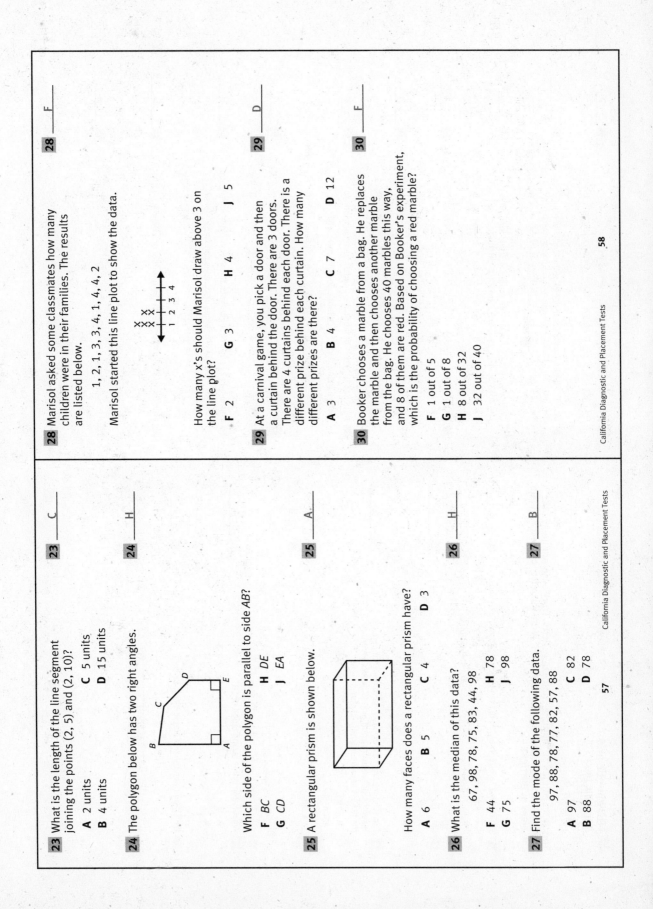

23 What is the length of the line segment joining the points (2, 5) and (2, 10)?

  A 2 units   **C** 5 units
  B 4 units   **D** 15 units

23 ____ C

24 The polygon below has two right angles.

Which side of the polygon is parallel to side *AB?*

  F *BC*   **H** *DE*
  G *CD*   **J** *EA*

24 ____ H

25 A rectangular prism is shown below.

How many faces does a rectangular prism have?

  A 6   **B** 5   **C** 4   **D** 3

25 ____ A

26 What is the median of this data?

  67, 98, 78, 75, 83, 44, 98

  F 44   **H** 78
  G 75   **J** 98

26 ____ H

27 Find the mode of the following data.

  97, 88, 78, 77, 82, 57, 88

  A 97   **C** 82
  B 88   **D** 78

27 ____ B

57 California Diagnostic and Placement Tests

28 Marisol asked some classmates how many children were in their families. The results are listed below.

  1, 2, 1, 3, 3, 4, 1, 4, 4, 2

  Marisol started this line plot to show the data.

How many x's should Marisol draw above 3 on the line plot?

  F 2   **G** 3   **H** 4   **J** 5

28 ____ F

29 At a carnival game, you pick a door and then a curtain behind the door. There are 3 doors. There are 4 curtains behind each door. There is a different prize behind each curtain. How many different prizes are there?

  A 3   **B** 4   **C** 7   **D** 12

29 ____ D

30 Booker chooses a marble from a bag. He replaces the marble and then chooses another marble from the bag. He chooses 40 marbles this way, and 8 of them are red. Based on Booker's experiment, which is the probability of choosing a red marble?

  F 1 out of 5
  G 1 out of 8
  H 8 out of 32
  J 32 out of 40

30 ____ F

58 California Diagnostic and Placement Tests

Answers (Grade 6)

Diagnostic and Placement

Grade 6

Name _____

Date _____

This test contains 30 multiple-choice questions. Work each problem in the space on this page. Select the best answer. Write the letter of the answer on the blank at the right.

1 What is 4,738,526 rounded to the nearest hundred thousand?

A 5,000,000   C 4,739,000
B 4,740,000   D 4,700,000

1 ___D___

2 What is 30% of 330?

F 99   H 300
G 110   J 990

2 ___F___

3 The school band sold 200 tickets to their concert. If 90 of the tickets were adult tickets, what percent of the tickets sold were adult tickets?

A 18%   C 55%
B 45%   D 90%

3 ___B___

4 $6^4 =$

F $6 + 6 + 6 + 6$ H $4 + 4 + 4 + 4 + 4 + 4$
G $6 \times 6 \times 6 \times 6$ J $4 \times 4 \times 4 \times 4 \times 4 \times 4$

4 ___G___

5 What is the prime factorization of 18?

A 3×6 C 2×3^3
B 2×9 D 2×3^2

5 ___D___

6 Which point on the number line is located at −3?

```
   R   S       T   U
 |---|---|---|---|---|
-4      0       4
```

F R   H T
G S   J U

6 ___F___

7 $3.45 \times 2.6 =$

A 8.64   B 8.97   C 86.4   D 89.7

7 ___B___

8 Mateo ordered 4 ham sandwiches at the deli. The total amount was $30.52. How much did each sandwich cost?

F $7.63   G $7.83   H $12.63   J $122.08

8 ___F___

9 Chrissy is knitting a scarf. The scarf is 4.6 feet long. If she knits another 1.75 feet, how long will the scarf be?

A 6.35 feet   B 5.81 feet   C 5.35 feet   D 2.85 feet

9 ___A___

10 $29,412 \div 43 =$

F 684   G 698   H 703   J 730

10 ___F___

11 $4\frac{1}{4} + 1\frac{1}{3} =$

A $5\frac{1}{7}$ B $5\frac{1}{6}$ C $5\frac{2}{7}$ D $5\frac{7}{12}$

11 ___D___

12 Nate had $6\frac{3}{5}$ yards of fabric. He used $3\frac{1}{2}$ yards of fabric to make a pillow. How much fabric does he have left?

F $3\frac{1}{10}$ yards   G $3\frac{1}{5}$ yards   H $3\frac{2}{3}$ yards   J $4\frac{1}{10}$ yards

12 ___F___

13 $\frac{3}{4} \times \frac{2}{5} =$

A $\frac{3}{10}$ B $\frac{7}{20}$ C $\frac{5}{9}$ D $1\frac{7}{8}$

13 ___A___

14 Isabel has $2\frac{1}{8}$ cups of sugar. Each batch of cookies uses $\frac{3}{4}$ cup of sugar. How many batches of cookies can Isabel bake?

F $1\frac{3}{8}$ G $1\frac{19}{32}$ H $2\frac{5}{6}$ J $2\frac{7}{8}$

14 ___H___

15 Which expression represents the quotient of 31 and a number?

A $31 \times n$ C $31 - n$
B $31 + n$ D $31 \div n$

15 ___D___

16 If $y = 4$, what is the value of $y \times 7 + 3$?

F 24   G 25   H 31   J 40

16 ___H___

Answers (Grade 6)

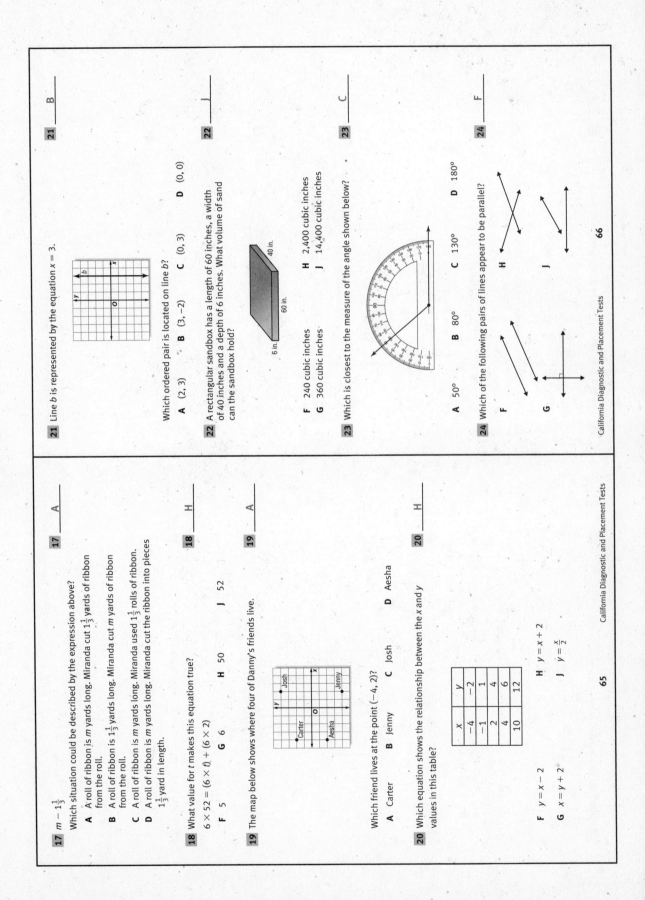

17 $m - 1\frac{1}{3}$

17 _____ A

Which situation could be described by the expression above?

A A roll of ribbon is m yards long. Miranda cut $1\frac{1}{3}$ yards of ribbon from the roll.

B A roll of ribbon is $1\frac{1}{3}$ yards long. Miranda cut m yards of ribbon from the roll.

C A roll of ribbon is m yards long. Miranda used $1\frac{1}{3}$ rolls of ribbon.

D A roll of ribbon is m yards long. Miranda cut the ribbon into pieces $1\frac{1}{3}$ yard in length.

18 What value for t makes this equation true?

18 _____ H

$6 \times 52 = (6 \times t) + (6 \times 2)$

F 5   G 6   H 50   J 52

19 The map below shows where four of Danny's friends live.

19 _____ A

Which friend lives at the point $(-4, 2)$?

A Carter   B Jenny   C Josh   D Aesha

20 Which equation shows the relationship between the x and y values in this table?

20 _____ H

x	y
−4	−2
−1	1
2	4
4	6
10	12

F $y = x - 2$

G $x = y + 2$

H $y = x + 2$

J $y = \frac{x}{2}$

21 Line b is represented by the equation $x = 3$.

21 _____ B

Which ordered pair is located on line b?

A (2, 3)   B (3, −2)   C (0, 3)   D (0, 0)

22 A rectangular sandbox has a length of 60 inches, a width of 40 inches and a depth of 6 inches. What volume of sand can the sandbox hold?

22 _____ J

F 240 cubic inches   H 2,400 cubic inches

G 360 cubic inches   J 14,400 cubic inches

23 Which is closest to the measure of the angle shown below?

23 _____ C

A 50°   B 80°   C 130°   D 180°

24 Which of the following pairs of lines appear to be parallel?

24 _____ F

F   G   H   J

Answers (Grade 6)

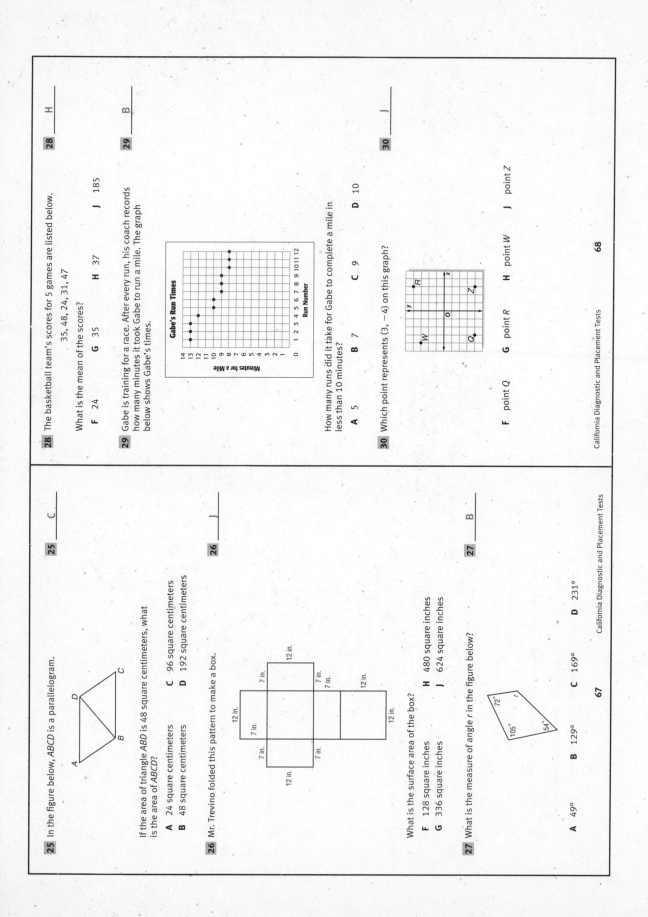

25 _C_

In the figure below, _ABCD_ is a parallelogram.

If the area of triangle _ABD_ is 48 square centimeters, what is the area of _ABCD?_

A 24 square centimeters
B 48 square centimeters
C 96 square centimeters
D 192 square centimeters

26 _J_

Mr. Trevino folded this pattern to make a box.

12 in. 7 in. 12 in.

What is the surface area of the box?

F 128 square inches
G 336 square inches
H 480 square inches
J 624 square inches

27 _B_

What is the measure of angle _r_ in the figure below?

72° 105° 54° _r_

A 49°
B 129°
C 169°
D 231°

28 _H_

The basketball team's scores for 5 games are listed below.

35, 48, 24, 31, 47

What is the mean of the scores?

F 24 G 35 H 37 J 185

29 _B_

Gabe is training for a race. After every run, his coach records how many minutes it took Gabe to run a mile. The graph below shows Gabe's times.

Gabe's Run Times

Minutes for a Mile

Run Number

How many runs did it take for Gabe to complete a mile in less than 10 minutes?

A 5 B 7 C 9 D 10

30 _J_

Which point represents (3, −4) on this graph?

F point _Q_ G point _R_ H point _W_ J point _Z_

Answers (Grade 7)

Diagnostic and Placement
Grade 7

Name _____

Date _____

This test contains 30 multiple-choice questions. Work each problem in the space on this page. Select the best answer. Write the letter of the answer on the blank at the right.

1 Which set of numbers is in order from least to greatest?

A $-3.1, -\frac{3}{8}, \frac{5}{8}, \frac{4}{5}$

B $-\frac{3}{8}, -3.1, \frac{5}{8}, \frac{4}{5}$

C $\frac{4}{5}, \frac{5}{8}, -\frac{3}{8}, -3.1$

D $-3.1, -\frac{3}{8}, \frac{4}{5}, \frac{5}{8}$

1 ___ A ___

2 Which number could be the value of point A?

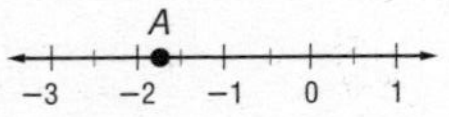

A
●
-3 -2 -1   0   1

F $-2\frac{1}{4}$

G -2

H $-1\frac{3}{4}$

J $-1\frac{1}{4}$

2 ___ H ___

3 For every 12 slices of pizza sold at Ping's Pizza Shop, 3 are pepperoni, 4 are sausage, and the rest are cheese. What is the ratio of pepperoni to cheese?

A 3:12

B 3:5

C 3:4

D 5:3

3 ___ B ___

4 Horatio jogs 5 laps around a track in 8 minutes. At the same rate, how long would it take him to jog 12 laps?

F 15 minutes

G 15.6 minutes

H 19.2 minutes

J 20 minutes

4 ___ H ___

5 Marita earned $50 for baby-sitting 8 hours. At the same rate how much would she earn for baby-sitting 10 hours?

A $60.00

B $60.25

C $62.00

D $62.50

5 ___ D ___

73 California Diagnostic and Placement Tests

6 Aleta went to dinner. The bill was $36. She gave the waiter a 15% tip. What was the total amount Aleta spent on the food and the tip?

F $36.15

G $37.50

H $38.40

J $41.40

6 ___ J ___

7 Sara walked $1\frac{3}{10}$ miles to her friend's house. Then she walked $\frac{3}{4}$ mile to the library. How far did Sara walk in all?

A $1\frac{3}{7}$ miles

B $1\frac{9}{10}$ miles

C $2\frac{1}{20}$ miles

D $2\frac{1}{10}$ miles

7 ___ C ___

8 Which multiplication is shown by the picture below?

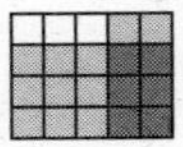

F $\frac{1}{5} \times \frac{1}{4}$

G $\frac{2}{5} \times \frac{3}{5}$

H $\frac{2}{20} \times \frac{3}{20}$

J $\frac{2}{5} \times \frac{3}{4}$

8 ___ J ___

9 Alvin was testing an elevator in a new office building. He started on the 1st floor. He rode the elevator up 5 floors, then down 3 floors, then up 7 floors, and then down 1 floor. On what floor did he stop?

A 8th floor

B 9th floor

C 15th floor

D 17th floor

9 ___ B ___

10 Simplify $-8 + 17(-3)$.

F -59

G -28

H -27

J 6

10 ___ F ___

11 Kono divided the numerator and denominator of $\frac{48}{72}$ by the same number to simplify the fraction in one step. By what number did he divide?

A 2

B 12

C 16

D 24

11 ___ D ___

74 California Diagnostic and Placement Tests

Answers (Grade 7)

20 A triangle has a height that is 3 units longer than its base. If b represents the base and h represents the height, which equation represents the area of the triangle?

F $A = \frac{1}{2}(b + 3)$ **H** $A = \frac{1}{2}b(b + 3)$

G $A = \frac{1}{2}(h + 3)$ **J** $A = \frac{1}{2}(h + 3)$

21 A circle has a radius of 8 centimeters. What is the circumference of the circle?

A 8π centimeters   **C** 64π centimeters

B 16π centimeters   **D** 128π centimeters

22 The can shown below is a cylinder.

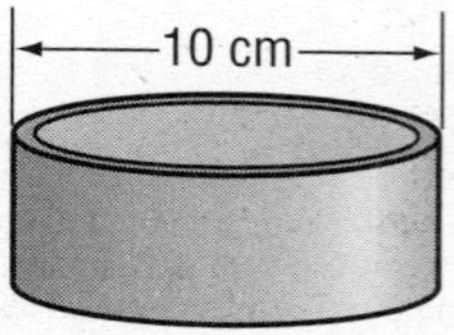

10 cm

Which is the best estimation for the area of the top of the can?

F 25 cm²   **H** 75 cm²

G 30 cm²   **J** 100 cm²

23 In the diagram below, which is a pair of vertical angles?

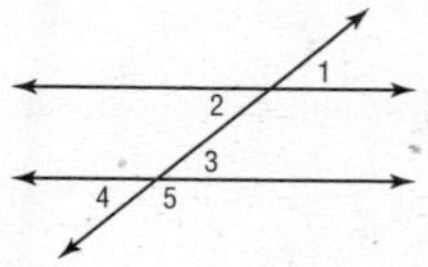

A $\angle 1$ and $\angle 2$ **C** $\angle 1$ and $\angle 4$

B $\angle 1$ and $\angle 3$ **D** $\angle 1$ and $\angle 5$

20	H
21	B
22	H
23	A

---

12 If $12x = 99$, what is the value of x?

F $0.1\overline{2}$ **H** 87

G 8.25   **J** 1188

13 What is the solution to the equation $-8 + p = -2$?

A $p = -10$ **C** $p = 6$

B $p = -6$ **D** $p = 10$

14 Erin has 87 baseball cards in her collection. Erin's number of cards is x less than Oscar's number of cards. Which expression represents Oscar's number of cards?

F $87 + x$ **H** $x - 87$

G $87 - x$ **J** $87x$

15 What is the value of the expression below?

$$16 - 3(8 + 2)^2$$

A -884 **C** -188

B -284 **D** 1300

16 Simplify the expression $7^2 - 4^2 \times 3$.

F -10 **H** 18

G 1   **J** 99

17 A package weighs $2\frac{3}{4}$ pounds. What is the weight of the package in ounces?

A 35 ounces   **C** 43.7 ounces

B 36.8 ounces   **D** 44 ounces

18 Which of the following boxes of cereal costs the least per ounce?

F 10 ounces for $3.19   **H** 15 ounces for $4.59

G 12 ounces for $3.49   **J** 20 ounces for $5.99

19 A landscaper covers 8,400 square feet with fertilizer in 45 minutes. At the same rate, how many square feet would she cover in 1 hour?

A 10,500 square feet   **C** 12,600 square feet

B 11,200 square feet   **D** 18,667 square feet

12	G
13	C
14	F
15	B
16	G
17	D
18	G
19	B

Answers (Grade 7)

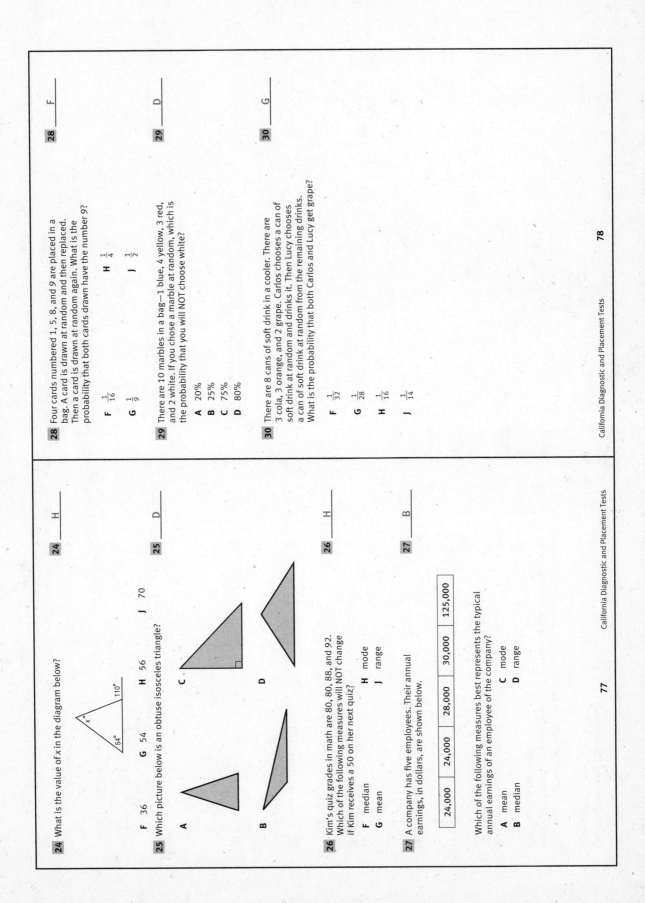

24 What is the value of *x* in the diagram below?

54° *x*° 110°

F 36   **G** 54   **H** 56   **J** 70

24 _____ H

25 Which picture below is an obtuse isosceles triangle?

A

B

C

D

25 _____ D

26 Kim's quiz grades in math are 80, 80, 88, and 92. Which of the following measures will NOT change if Kim receives a 50 on her next quiz?

F median   **H** mode
G mean   **J** range

26 _____ H

27 A company has five employees. Their annual earnings, in dollars, are shown below.

| 24,000 | 24,000 | 28,000 | 30,000 | 125,000 |

Which of the following measures best represents the typical annual earnings of an employee of the company?

A mean   **C** mode
B median   **D** range

27 _____ B

28 Four cards numbered 1, 5, 8, and 9 are placed in a bag. A card is drawn at random and then replaced. Then a card is drawn at random again. What is the probability that both cards drawn have the number 9?

F $\frac{1}{16}$ **H** $\frac{1}{4}$

G $\frac{1}{9}$ **J** $\frac{1}{2}$

28 _____ F

29 There are 10 marbles in a bag—1 blue, 4 yellow, 3 red, and 2 white. If you chose a marble at random, which is the probability that you will NOT choose white?

A 20%
B 25%
C 75%
D 80%

29 _____ D

30 There are 8 cans of soft drink in a cooler. There are 3 cola, 3 orange, and 2 grape. Carlos chooses a can of soft drink at random and drinks it. Then Lucy chooses a can of soft drink at random from the remaining drinks. What is the probability that both Carlos and Lucy get grape?

F $\frac{1}{32}$

G $\frac{1}{28}$

H $\frac{1}{16}$

J $\frac{1}{14}$

30 _____ G

Answers (Algebra 1)

Diagnostic and Placement
Algebra 1

Name _____
Date _____

This test contains 30 multiple-choice questions. Work each problem in the space on this page. Select the best answer. Write the letter of the answer on the blank at the right.

1 Which set of numbers is in order from least to greatest?

A $2.07 \times 10^4, 2.07 \times 10^{-3}, -2.07 \times 10^{-2}, -2.07 \times 10^2$
B $2.07 \times 10^{-3}, -2.07 \times 10^{-2}, -2.07 \times 10^2, 2.07 \times 10^4$
C $-2.07 \times 10^2, -2.07 \times 10^{-2}, 2.07 \times 10^{-3}, 2.07 \times 10^4$
D $-2.07 \times 10^{-2}, -2.07 \times 10^2, 2.07 \times 10^{-3}, 2.07 \times 10^4$

1 ___ C

2 $3\frac{3}{5} \cdot \frac{2}{5} - (0.4)^2 =$

F -0.16 H 7.4
G 1.28 J 8.84

2 ___ J

3 Luis saved $\frac{5}{8}$ of his pay. What percent of his pay did he save?

A 6.25% C 62.5%
B 40% D 72.5%

3 ___ C

4 Which is an irrational number?

F $\sqrt{2}$ H $5\frac{4}{9}$
G $\sqrt{9}$ J 3^2

4 ___ F

5 $0.04 =$

A $\frac{1}{40}$ C $\frac{1}{4}$
B $\frac{1}{25}$ D $\frac{2}{5}$

5 ___ B

6 A bookstore manager paid $12 for a book and used a 60% markup to set the regular price of the book. Jamie bought the book from the store for 10% off of the regular price. How much did Jamie pay for the book?

F $17.28   H $19.20
G $18.00   J $20.40

6 ___ F

7 $\dfrac{\left(\frac{4}{5}\right)^{-3} \times \left(\frac{4}{5}\right)^8}{\left(\frac{4}{5}\right)^2} =$

A $\left(\frac{4}{5}\right)^{-48}$ C $\left(\frac{4}{5}\right)^3$
B $\left(\frac{4}{5}\right)^{-12}$ D $\left(\frac{4}{5}\right)^7$

7 ___ C

8 $\dfrac{8}{65} + \dfrac{1}{25} =$

F $\frac{9}{325}$ H $\frac{53}{325}$
G $\frac{1}{10}$ J $\frac{49}{65}$

8 ___ H

9 $\dfrac{2^2 \cdot 8^2}{2^{-1} \cdot 5^{-2} \cdot 8^3} =$

A 0.04 C 18.75
B 10 D 25

9 ___ D

10 A square garden has an area of 144 square feet. What is the length of one side of the garden?

F 3 feet   H 36 feet
G 12 feet   J 72 feet

10 ___ G

11 $-|12 - 5| + |3 - 8| =$

A -12 C 2
B -2 D 12

11 ___ B

12 Which algebraic expression represents the phrase "6 less than the sum of x and the square of x"?

F $x + x^2 - 6$ H $6 - x + x^2$
G $x + \sqrt{x} - 6$ J $6 - (x + x^2)$

12 ___ F

13 Given $a = 3$ and $b = -5$, evaluate $4a - 2(b + 3)$.

A -20 C 8
B -8 D 16

13 ___ D

Answers (Algebra 1)

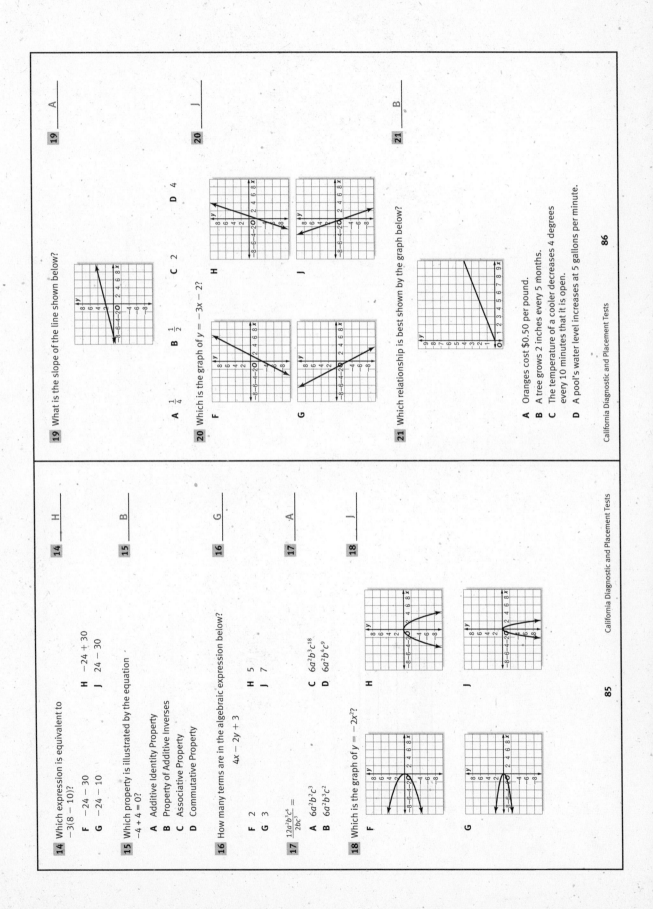

14 Which expression is equivalent to $-3(8 - 10)$?

F $-24 - 30$ **H** $-24 + 30$

G $-24 - 10$ **J** $24 - 30$

         14   H

15 Which property is illustrated by the equation $-4 + 4 = 0$?

A Additive Identity Property

B Property of Additive Inverses

C Associative Property

D Commutative Property

         15   B

16 How many terms are in the algebraic expression below?

$$4x - 2y + 3$$

F 2   **H** 5

G 3   **J** 7

         16   G

17 $\dfrac{12a^2b^2c^6}{2bc^3} =$

A $6a^2b^2c^3$ **C** $6a^2b^3c^{18}$

B $6a^2b^3c^2$ **D** $6a^2b^4c^9$

         17   A

18 Which is the graph of $y = -2x^2$?

         18   J

19 What is the slope of the line shown below?

A $\frac{1}{4}$ **B** $\frac{1}{2}$ **C** 2   **D** 4

         19   A

20 Which is the graph of $y = -3x - 2$?

         20   J

21 Which relationship is best shown by the graph below?

A Oranges cost $0.50 per pound.

B A tree grows 2 inches every 5 months.

C The temperature of a cooler decreases 4 degrees every 10 minutes that it is open.

D A pool's water level increases at 5 gallons per minute.

         21   B

Answers (Algebra 1)

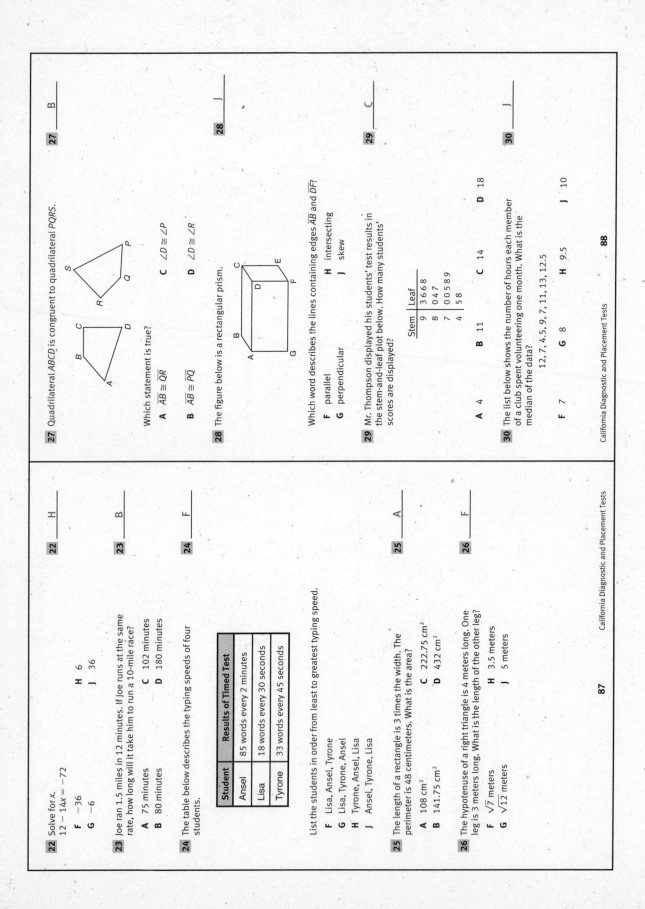

22 Solve for x.
12 − 14x = −72

F −36   H 6
G −6   J 36

22 _____ **H**

23 Joe ran 1.5 miles in 12 minutes. If Joe runs at the same rate, how long will it take him to run a 10-mile race?

A 75 minutes   C 102 minutes
B 80 minutes   D 180 minutes

23 _____ **B**

24 The table below describes the typing speeds of four students.

Student	Results of Timed Test
Ansel	85 words every 2 minutes
Lisa	18 words every 30 seconds
Tyrone	33 words every 45 seconds

List the students in order from least to greatest typing speed.

F Lisa, Ansel, Tyrone
G Lisa, Tyrone, Ansel
H Tyrone, Ansel, Lisa
J Ansel, Tyrone, Lisa

24 _____ **F**

25 The length of a rectangle is 3 times the width. The perimeter is 48 centimeters. What is the area?

A 108 cm²   C 222.75 cm²
B 141.75 cm²   D 432 cm²

25 _____ **A**

26 The hypotenuse of a right triangle is 4 meters long. One leg is 3 meters long. What is the length of the other leg?

F $\sqrt{7}$ meters   H 3.5 meters
G $\sqrt{12}$ meters   J 5 meters

26 _____ **F**

27 Quadrilateral ABCD is congruent to quadrilateral PQRS.

Which statement is true?

A $\overline{AB} \cong \overline{QR}$ C $\angle D \cong \angle P$
B $\overline{AB} \cong \overline{PQ}$ D $\angle D \cong \angle R$

27 _____ **B**

28 The figure below is a rectangular prism.

Which word describes the lines containing edges $\overline{AB}$ and $\overline{DF}$?

F parallel   H intersecting
G perpendicular   J skew

28 _____ **J**

29 Mr. Thompson displayed his students' test results in the stem-and-leaf plot below. How many students' scores are displayed?

Stem	Leaf
9	3 6 6 8
8	0 4 7
7	0 0 5 8 9
4	5 8

A 4   B 11   C 14   D 18

29 _____ **C**

30 The list below shows the number of hours each member of a club spent volunteering one month. What is the median of the data?

12, 7, 4.5, 9, 7, 11, 13, 12.5

F 7   G 8   H 9.5   J 10

30 _____ **J**

Diagnostic and Placement Geometry

Name _____
Date _____

This test contains 30 multiple-choice questions. Work each problem in the space on this page. Select the best answer. Write the letter of the answer on the blank at the right.

1 Which expression is equivalent to $-\frac{1}{2}\left(8-\frac{1}{2}\right)$?

A $-4+\frac{1}{4}$ C $7\frac{1}{2}+\frac{1}{4}$

B $-4-1$ D $7\frac{1}{2}-1$

1 _____ A

2 Simplify $\frac{\sqrt{a}\cdot b^2}{a^2 b^5}$.

F $a^{\frac{1}{3}}b^{\frac{5}{2}}$ H $\frac{1}{ab^3}$

G $a^{\frac{3}{2}}b^{10}$ J $\frac{1}{a^{\frac{1}{2}}b^3}$

2 _____ H

3 What are the solutions to the equation $|x-3|-8=-1$?

A $x=-5; x=11$ C $x=7; x=-7$

B $x=-4; x=10$ D $x=10; x=-10$

3 _____ B

4 $2(3x-1)-3(x+5)=$

F $2x-17$ H $3x-17$

G $3x-16$ J $4x+3$

4 _____ H

5 Emily is considering two job offers. Company A will pay $200 per week plus a 6% commission on all sales. Company B will pay $320 per week plus a 4% commission on all sales. If x represents the dollar amount of sales, which inequality can be solved to find how much Emily will need to sell in a week to earn more by working for Company A?

A $0.02x > 120$ C $0.10x > 120$

B $0.02x > 520$ D $0.10x > 520$

5 _____ A

6 Which of the following is an example of inductive reasoning?

F Every rectangle is a parallelogram. Every square is a rectangle. Therefore, every square is a parallelogram.

G If $x > 3$, then $x^2 > y$. Therefore, $4^2 > y$.

H Ted's bus arrived at his bus stop before 8:05 A.M. every morning for two weeks. Ted decides that his bus will arrive before 8:05 A.M. the next morning.

J Keisha's uncle promises to give her $5 if she gets a grade of 85 or higher on her math test. Keisha gets a 93 on her math test. Then Keisha's uncle gives her $5.

6 _____ H

7 Which of the following is a counterexample that shows the statement $2x \geq x$ is false?

A $x=-1$ B $x=0$ C $x=1$ D $x=2$

7 _____ A

8 Which of the following shows a true statement and the correct property to justify that statement?

F $2(x+8)=2x+8$; Distributive Property

G $2(x+8)=2x+16$; Distributive Property

H $2(x+8)=(2x)+8$; Associative Property

J $2(x+8)=(2x)+16$; Associative Property

8 _____ G

9 For what value or values of x is the following statement true?

$$|x^2-1| = -(x^2-1)$$

A only -1 and 1 C all negative real numbers

B all real numbers   D no real numbers

9 _____ A

10 Which is the graph of $3x-2y \leq -6$?

F   G   H   J

10 _____ J

Answers (Geometry)

11 Which point lies on the line whose equation is $x - 3y = 6$?

  A $(-3, 3)$ **C** $(-3, 9)$
  B $(3, -1)$ **D** $(9, -1)$

11 _____ B

12 Which is an equation of the line that has a slope of $-\frac{1}{3}$ and passes through the point $(-5, 2)$?

  F $x - 3y = -11$ **H** $x + 3y = 1$
  G $x - 3y = 11$ **J** $x + 3y = 21$

12 _____ H

13 Which is an equation of the line that passes through the point $(1, 2)$ and is perpendicular to the line defined by $2x + 5y = 10$?

  A $2x + 5y = -12$ **C** $5x - 2y = -1$
  B $2x + 5y = 12$ **D** $5x - 2y = 1$

13 _____ D

14 What is the x-coordinate of the solution of the following system of equations?

$$2x + y = 3$$
$$3x - 2y = 4$$

  F $x = \frac{1}{7}$ **H** $x = 2$
  G $x = \frac{10}{7}$ **J** $x = 3$

14 _____ G

15 Which shows the solution set of the following system of inequalities?

$$x - y \leq -1$$
$$x + 2y \leq 0$$

  A
  C

  B
  D

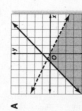
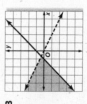

15 _____ B

16 $(x - 1)(x - 2) - (x^2 - 1) =$

  F $-2x - 1$ **H** $-3x - 1$
  G $-2x + 1$ **J** $-3x + 3$

16 _____ J

17 $9x^3 - x =$

  A $x(3x + 1)(3x - 1)$ **C** $x(3x - 1)^2$
  B $x(9x - 1)(x - 1)$ **D** $x(9x - 1)^2$

17 _____ A

18 What are the solutions to the equation $2x^2 + 9x = 5$?

  F $x = -1, x = \frac{5}{2}$ **H** $x = 5, x = -\frac{1}{2}$
  G $x = 1, x = -\frac{5}{2}$ **J** $x = -5, x = \frac{1}{2}$

18 _____ J

19 Ray wants to solve the equation $x^2 - 6x + 1 = 0$ by the method of completing the square. His first step is shown below.

$$x^2 - 6x + 1 = 0$$
$$x^2 - 6x = -1$$

Which of the following shows the next step?

  A $x(x - 6) = -1$ **C** $x^2 - 6x - 9 = -1 - 9$
  B $x^2 = 6x - 1$ **D** $x^2 - 6x + 9 = -1 + 9$

19 _____ D

20 The quadratic formula gives an expression for the solutions to the equation $ax^2 + bx + c = 0$. The first two steps in deriving the quadratic formula are shown below.

$$ax^2 + bx + c = 0$$
$$ax^2 + bx = -c$$
$$x^2 + \frac{b}{a}x = -\frac{c}{a}$$

Which of the following choices describes the next step in deriving the formula?

  F Add $\frac{b^2}{4a^2}$ to both sides of the equation.

  G Add $-\frac{b}{2a}$ to both sides of the equation.

  H Divide both sides of the equation by 2.

  J Add $\sqrt{b^2 - 4ac}$ to both sides of the equation.

20 _____ F

Answers (Geometry)

21 ___ D

22 ___ H

23 ___ A

24 ___ H

25 ___ A

26 ___ J

21 What are the solutions of the equation $x^2 - 5x - 1 = 0$?

A $\dfrac{-5+\sqrt{21}}{2}$ and $\dfrac{-5-\sqrt{21}}{2}$

B $\dfrac{-5+\sqrt{29}}{2}$ and $\dfrac{-5-\sqrt{29}}{2}$

C $\dfrac{5+\sqrt{21}}{2}$ and $\dfrac{5-\sqrt{21}}{2}$

D $\dfrac{5+\sqrt{29}}{2}$ and $\dfrac{5-\sqrt{29}}{2}$

22 Which is a zero (root) of the polynomial $2x^2 - x - 5$?

F $\dfrac{1-\sqrt{41}}{4}$ H $\dfrac{1-\sqrt{41}}{4}$

G $\dfrac{-1+\sqrt{41}}{2}$ J $\dfrac{-1+\sqrt{41}}{4}$

23 An x-intercept of the graph of $y = x^2 - x + c$ is -6. What is the value of c?

A -42 C -2

B -30 D 3

24 If an object is thrown upward with an initial velocity of 40 feet per second from a height of 56 feet, its height h is given by the equation $h = -16t^2 + 40t + 56$. In the equation, h is the height in feet and t is the time in seconds after the object is thrown. (Air resistance is neglected.) How many seconds will it take for the object to hit the ground after it is thrown?

F 1 second   H 3.5 seconds

G 3.1 seconds   J 7 seconds

25 Simplify $\dfrac{x^2-1}{x^2+x-2}$.

A $\dfrac{x+1}{x+2}$ C $\dfrac{x-1}{x+2}$

B $\dfrac{x+1}{x-2}$ D $\dfrac{x-1}{x-2}$

26 $\dfrac{x}{x+3} + \dfrac{2}{x^2-9} =$

F $\dfrac{x+2}{x^2+x-12}$ H $\dfrac{x^2-3x+2}{x^2-9}$

G $\dfrac{x^3-9x}{2x-6}$ J $\dfrac{x^2+3x+2}{x^2-9}$

27 ___ D

28 ___ H

29 ___ C

30 ___ G

27 Solve $\dfrac{1}{x-5} - \dfrac{3}{x} = \dfrac{1}{x}$.

A $x = \dfrac{3}{20}$ C $x = \dfrac{5}{2}$

B $x = \dfrac{2}{5}$ D $x = \dfrac{20}{3}$

28 Teva has 500 milliliters of a juice drink that is 20% grape juice. She also has some juice drink that is 50% grape juice. How many milliliters of the 50% mixture must she add to 500 milliliters of the 20% mixture to get a mixture that is 25% grape juice?

F 12.5 milliliters   H 100 milliliters

G 62.5 milliliters   J 150 milliliters

29 Which equation does NOT define y as a function of x?

A $y = x^2$ C $x = y^2$

B $y = x + 5$ D $x = y + 5$

30 What is the domain of the function $f(x) = \dfrac{3}{x+2}$?

F the set of all real numbers

G the set of all real numbers except $x = -2$

H the set of all real numbers except $x = 0$

J the set of all real numbers except $x = 2$

Answers (Algebra 2)

Diagnostic and Placement
Algebra 2

Name _____
Date _____

This test contains 30 multiple-choice questions. Work each problem in the space on this page. Select the best answer. Write the letter of the answer on the blank at the right.

1 Simplify $(x^{\frac{1}{3}})^4(x^{\frac{1}{3}})\sqrt{xy}$.

A $x\sqrt{xy}$
B $x^2\sqrt{xy}$
C $x^3\sqrt{y}$
D $x^{\frac{11}{2}}\sqrt{y}$

1 ____ C

2 What are the solutions to the equation $-2|x-3| = -10$?

F $x = 5; x = -5$
G $x = 8; x = -8$
H $x = 8; x = -2$
J no solution

2 ____ H

3 Simplify the expression $4(2x-1) - 3(x+5)$.

A $3x - 19$
B $5x - 16$
C $5x - 19$
D $9x - 2$

3 ____ C

4 Use the equation $C = \frac{5}{9}(F-32)$ to convert 11°C to Fahrenheit.

F $-12.2°F$
G $-11.7°F$
H $38.1°F$
J $51.8°F$

4 ____ J

5 Which is the graph of $5x + 3y = 6$?

A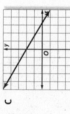

B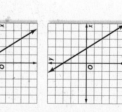

C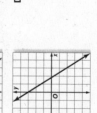

D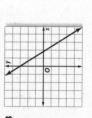

5 ____ A

6 Which is an equation of the line that has a slope of $\frac{1}{2}$ and passes through the point (3, −1)?

F $x + 2y = 1$
G $x + 2y = -1$
H $x - 2y = 5$
J $x - 2y = 8$

6 ____ H

7 What is the *y*-coordinate of the solution of the following system of equations?

$$2x - 5y = 0$$
$$x + 2y = -4$$

A $y = -1$
B $y = -\frac{8}{9}$
C $y = \frac{8}{3}$
D $y = 8$

7 ____ B

8 $(x + 2)(x^2 - 1) + x =$

F $x^2 + 2x + 1$
G $2x^2 + 2x - 2$
H $x^3 + x - 2$
J $x^3 + 2x^2 - 2$

8 ____ J

9 What are the solutions to the equation $3x^2 + 11x = 4$?

A $x = -\frac{1}{3}, x = 4$
B $x = \frac{1}{3}, x = -4$
C $x = -\frac{4}{3}, x = 1$
D $x = \frac{4}{3}, x = -1$

9 ____ B

10 The quadratic formula gives an expression for the solutions to the equation $ax^2 + bx + c = 0$. The first two steps in deriving the quadratic formula are shown below.

$$ax^2 + bx + c = 0$$
$$ax^2 + bx = -c$$
$$x^2 + \frac{b}{a}x = -\frac{c}{a}$$

Which of the following choices describes the next step in deriving the formula?

F Add $\frac{b^2}{4a^2}$ to both sides of the equation.
G Add $-\frac{b}{2a}$ to both sides of the equation.
H Add $-b$ to both sides of the equation.
J Add $\sqrt{b^2 - 4ac}$ to both sides of the equation.

10 ____ F

Answers (Algebra 2)

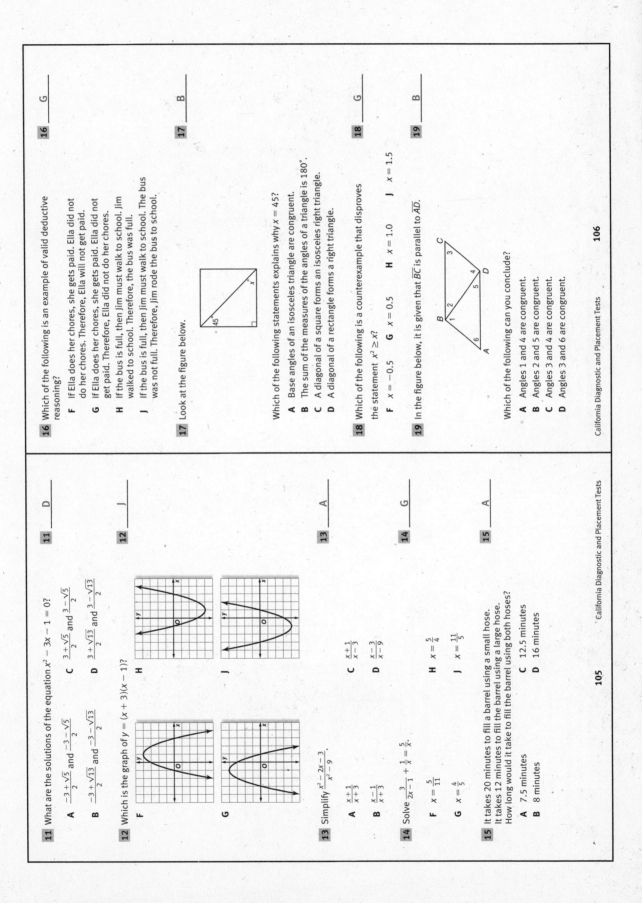

11 What are the solutions of the equation $x^2 - 3x - 1 = 0$?

A $\dfrac{-3+\sqrt{5}}{2}$ and $\dfrac{-3-\sqrt{5}}{2}$

B $\dfrac{-3+\sqrt{13}}{2}$ and $\dfrac{-3-\sqrt{13}}{2}$

C $\dfrac{3+\sqrt{5}}{2}$ and $\dfrac{3-\sqrt{5}}{2}$

D $\dfrac{3+\sqrt{13}}{2}$ and $\dfrac{3-\sqrt{13}}{2}$

11 _____ D

12 Which is the graph of $y = (x+3)(x-1)$?

F
G
H
J

12 _____ J

13 Simplify $\dfrac{x^2-2x-3}{x^2-9}$.

A $\dfrac{x+1}{x+3}$

B $\dfrac{x-1}{x+3}$

C $\dfrac{x+1}{x-3}$

D $\dfrac{x-3}{x-9}$

13 _____ A

14 Solve $\dfrac{3}{2x-1} + \dfrac{1}{x} = \dfrac{5}{x}$.

F $x = \dfrac{5}{11}$

G $x = \dfrac{4}{5}$

H $x = \dfrac{5}{4}$

J $x = \dfrac{11}{5}$

14 _____ G

15 It takes 20 minutes to fill a barrel using a small hose.
It takes 12 minutes to fill the barrel using a large hose.
How long would it take to fill the barrel using both hoses?

A 7.5 minutes
B 8 minutes
C 12.5 minutes
D 16 minutes

15 _____ A

16 Which of the following is an example of valid deductive reasoning?

F If Ella does her chores, she gets paid. Ella did not do her chores. Therefore, Ella will not get paid.

G If Ella does her chores, she gets paid. Ella did not get paid. Therefore, Ella did not do her chores.

H If the bus is full, then Jim must walk to school. Jim walked to school. Therefore, the bus was full.

J If the bus is full, then Jim must walk to school. The bus was not full. Therefore, Jim rode the bus to school.

16 _____ G

17 Look at the figure below.

Which of the following statements explains why $x = 45$?

A Base angles of an isosceles triangle are congruent.

B The sum of the measures of the angles of a triangle is $180°$.

C A diagonal of a square forms an isosceles right triangle.

D A diagonal of a rectangle forms a right triangle.

17 _____ B

18 Which of the following is a counterexample that disproves the statement $x^2 \geq x$?

F $x = -0.5$ G $x = 0.5$ H $x = 1.0$ J $x = 1.5$

18 _____ G

19 In the figure below, it is given that $\overline{BC}$ is parallel to $\overline{AD}$.

Which of the following can you conclude?

A Angles 1 and 4 are congruent.

B Angles 2 and 5 are congruent.

C Angles 3 and 4 are congruent.

D Angles 3 and 6 are congruent.

19 _____ B

Answers (Algebra 2)

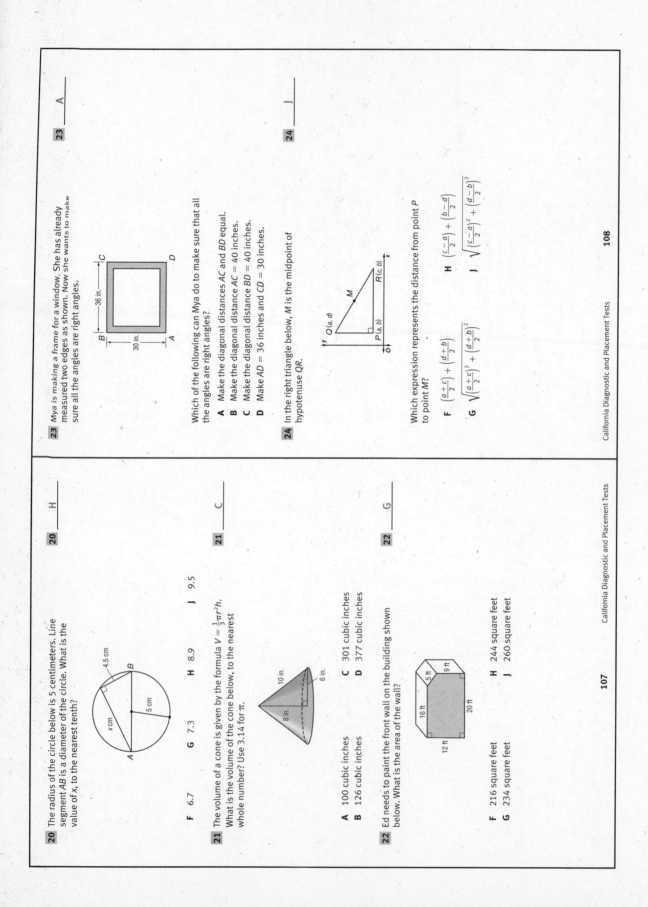

20 The radius of the circle below is 5 centimeters. Line segment *AB* is a diameter of the circle. What is the value of *x*, to the nearest tenth?

F 6.7   **G** 7.3   **H** 8.9   **J** 9.5

20 ____ H ____

21 The volume of a cone is given by the formula $V = \frac{1}{3}\pi r^2 h$. What is the volume of the cone below, to the nearest whole number? Use 3.14 for π.

A 100 cubic inches   **C** 301 cubic inches
B 126 cubic inches   **D** 377 cubic inches

21 ____ C ____

22 Ed needs to paint the front wall on the building shown below. What is the area of the wall?

F 216 square feet   **H** 244 square feet
G 234 square feet   **J** 260 square feet

22 ____ G ____

23 Mya is making a frame for a window. She has already measured two edges as shown. Now she wants to make sure all the angles are right angles.

Which of the following can Mya do to make sure that all the angles are right angles?

A Make the diagonal distances *AC* and *BD* equal.
B Make the diagonal distance *AC* = 40 inches.
C Make the diagonal distance *BD* = 40 inches.
D Make *AD* = 36 inches and *CD* = 30 inches.

23 ____ A ____

24 In the right triangle below, *M* is the midpoint of hypotenuse *QR*.

Which expression represents the distance from point *P* to point *M*?

F $\left(\frac{a+c}{2}\right) + \left(\frac{d+b}{2}\right)$ **H** $\left(\frac{c-a}{2}\right) + \left(\frac{b-d}{2}\right)$

G $\sqrt{\left(\frac{a+c}{2}\right)^2 + \left(\frac{d+b}{2}\right)^2}$ **J** $\sqrt{\left(\frac{c-a}{2}\right)^2 + \left(\frac{d-b}{2}\right)^2}$

24 ____ J ____

Answers (Algebra 2)

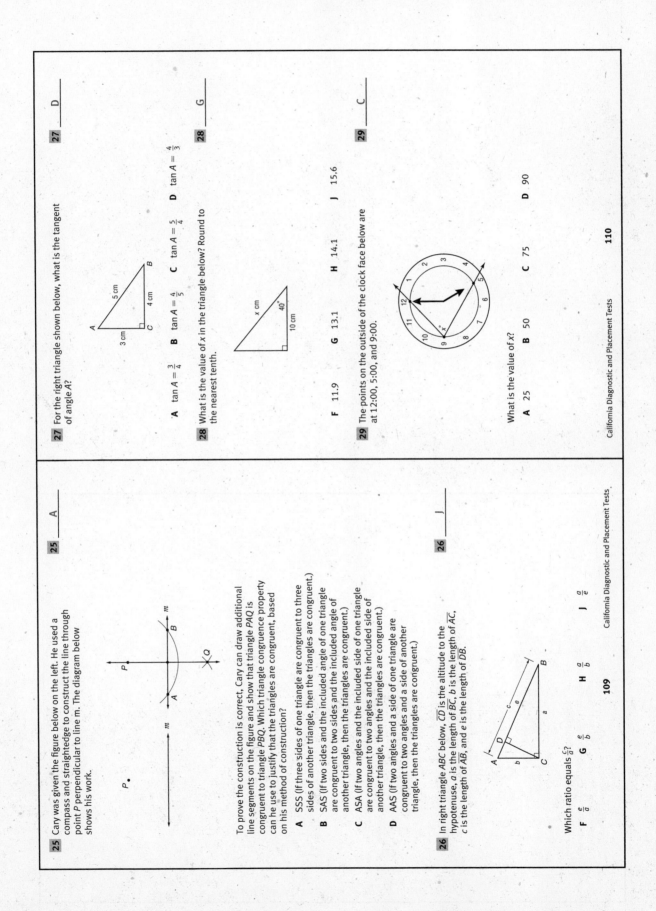

25. Cary was given the figure below on the left. He used a compass and straightedge to construct the line through point *P* perpendicular to line m. The diagram below shows his work.

25 _____ A

To prove the construction is correct, Cary can draw additional line segments on the figure and show that triangle *PAQ* is congruent to triangle *PBQ*. Which triangle congruence property can he use to justify that the triangles are congruent, based on his method of construction?

A SSS (If three sides of one triangle are congruent to three sides of another triangle, then the triangles are congruent.)

B SAS (If two sides and the included angle of one triangle are congruent to two sides and the included angle of another triangle, then the triangles are congruent.)

C ASA (If two angles and the included side of one triangle are congruent to two angles and the included side of another triangle, then the triangles are congruent.)

D AAS (If two angles and a side of one triangle are congruent to two angles and a side of another triangle, then the triangles are congruent.)

26. In right triangle *ABC* below, $\overline{CD}$ is the altitude to the hypotenuse, *a* is the length of $\overline{BC}$, *b* is the length of $\overline{AC}$, *c* is the length of $\overline{AB}$, and *e* is the length of $\overline{DB}$.

26 _____ J

Which ratio equals $\frac{c}{a}$?

F $\frac{e}{a}$ **G** $\frac{e}{b}$ **H** $\frac{a}{b}$ **J** $\frac{a}{e}$

27. For the right triangle shown below, what is the tangent of angle *A*?

27 _____ D

A $\tan A = \frac{3}{4}$ **B** $\tan A = \frac{4}{5}$ **C** $\tan A = \frac{5}{4}$ **D** $\tan A = \frac{4}{3}$

28. What is the value of *x* in the triangle below? Round to the nearest tenth.

28 _____ G

F 11.9   **G** 13.1   **H** 14.1   **J** 15.6

29. The points on the outside of the clock face below are at 12:00, 5:00, and 9:00.

29 _____ C

What is the value of *x*?

A 25   **B** 50   **C** 75   **D** 90

109

110

California Diagnostic and Placement Tests

California Diagnostic and Placement Tests

145

California Diagnostic and Placement Tests

Answers (Algebra 2)

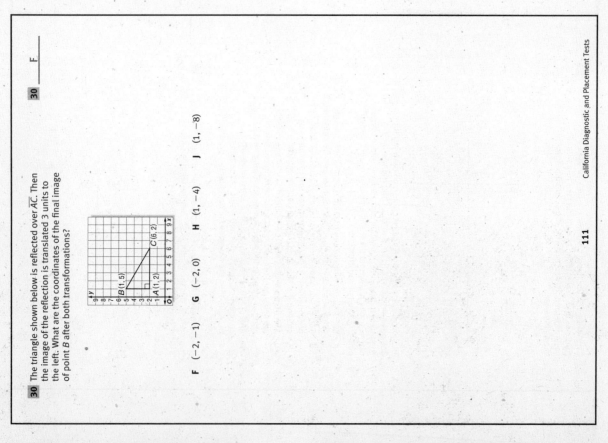

30 The triangle shown below is reflected over $\overline{AC}$. Then the image of the reflection is translated 3 units to the left. What are the coordinates of the final image of point B after both transformations?

F $(-2, -1)$ **G** $(-2, 0)$ **H** $(1, -4)$ **J** $(1, -8)$

30 _____ **F** _____